Restoring Old Radio Sets

by

Philip Lawson, G4FCL

Radio Society of Great Britain

Published by the Radio Society of Great Britain, 3 Abbey Court, Fraser Road, Priory Business Park, Bedford MK44 3WH. Tel 01234 832700 www.rsgb.org

ISBN: 9781 9101 9322 8

First published 2016

Layout and Edited by: Mike Browne, G3DIH

Cover Design: Kevin Williams, M6CYB

Production: Mark Allgar, M1MPA

Printed in Great Britain by Hobbs the Printers of Totton, Hampshire

Contents

Preface   v

Introduction   vi

Glossary   viii

1. An Example Radio Restoration Project   1

1.1 What Have We Got? – Let's Take a Good Look   1

1.2 Beginning Restoration Work   5

1.3 Does It Work?   6

1.4 Restoring the Cabinet   8

1.5 The Finished Item   9

2. Safety Matters   11

2.1 General Precautions   12

2.2 Electrical Shock   12

2.3 Physical Injury   12

2.4 Fire   13

2.5 Incapacity/Illness   13

2.6 Restored Equipment   13

3. What You Need to do the Job   15

3.1 Facilities   15

3.2 Tools   15

3.3 Materials   16

3.4 Parts   16

3.5 Test equipment   16

3.6 Cleaning Equipment   16

4. Beginning the Restoration Process   17

4.1 Stop! Put that Plug Down   17

4.2 Record What You See   18

4.3 Removing the Chassis from its Cabinet   18

4.4 Loose Dirt Removal   22

4.5 Restoration vs Rebuild   23

5. Chassis Hardware: Maintenance   25

  5.1 Dial Lamps   26

  5.2 Valves   26

  5.3 Tuning Dials   28

  5.4 Chassis Clean   29

  5.5 Tuner Drive Mechanism   30

  5.6 Wave-change switches   32

  5.7 Controls   34

6. Electrical repairs   37

  6.1 Resistors   37

  6.2 Capacitors   37

  6.3 Valves   39

  6.4 Internal Wiring   40

  6.5 Mains Cable   41

7. Electrical Testing   47

  7.1 Preparation & Safety Measures   47

  7.2 Switch-on   48

  7.3 Fault-Diagnosis   49

  7.4 Alignment & Calibration   52

8. Restoring the Cabinet   57

  8.1 Clean & Assess   57

  8.2 Bakelite   58

  8.3 Plastic   60

  8.4 Wood   62

9. Completing the job   67

  9.1 Final Assembly   67

  9.2 Care & Maintenance   69

References   70

Appendix   71

  Using a Multimeter – for Beginners   71

Preface

This book is an intense practical guide to the restoration of vintage radio sets of the type commonly found in the UK home between (roughly) the late 1920s and the late 1970s.

Assuming only a basic knowledge of electronics, it is designed to help the reader develop the skill and expertise needed to bring a vintage set back to working condition and to restore its cabinet. A route-map guides the reader through each stage, from initial assessment, through to care and maintenance of the finished item. Along the way, typical challenges the reader is likely to face are highlighted, and a wide range of techniques for tackling them discussed. Tools and materials needed to perform these tasks are identified, and important recommendations made as to the working environment. Considerable emphasis is placed on safety matters, owing to the diverse range of serious and potentially lethal hazards that are inherent in the restoration activity.

About The Author

Influenced by his father, who was a keen repairer of Black & White TV sets in his spare time, Philip naturally developed an interest in electronics at an early age. Licensed in the early 1970s, initially as G8ING and later as G4FCL, he was a keen member of Derby & District Amateur Radio Society, winning several trophies for amateur station operating and radio construction. After university Philip took up a professional career in electronic engineering and is now a Chartered Engineer with 20 years' experience leading RF, Microwave and Optical product development in telecoms, aerospace, and defence. He has published over 40 internal and external reports and his achievements include several world firsts.

Eur.Ing. **Philip Lawson** BSc(Eng) MSc CEng CPhys MIET MInstP PgDL LLM

Introduction

FOR MANY, seeing an old radio brings back happy memories of childhood, and visions of parents or grandparents gathered around it to listen to the classic entertainment programmes of yesteryear and the great broadcasts of wartime. For some, there is something special about the warm reassuring glow of the dial, the beautiful cabinet, and the rich tone, while for others there is a deeply personal attachment as the set or one similar, belonged to a dear and now lost family member. For a variety of reasons which will become apparent later, these old radio sets may well no longer work, and it is commonly assumed that they are destined either to become an ornament if they look nice, or for the skip if they do not.

But it does not have to be this way! It is often with surprise and a delight, that admirers learn that these old radios can be restored to life, enjoyed again, and become part of our heritage. Anyone with at least a basic knowledge of electronics, some soldering skill, an ability to read a circuit diagram, and the minimum of test equipment, can restore the most defunct and tatty looking old radio set back to life. Such a project need not be an expensive proposition either – I've rarely spent more than £50 per set on materials – but it is costly in terms of time and effort. For example, I was able to restore a highly-corroded woodworm-infested radio that had been in a garage for 30 years in one week, working on it (very hard!) full-time; but then I have the materials to hand and have had a lot of practice. Restoration is not a quick or easy task, and you are likely to experience the full range of emotions as problems occur and things go wrong; but as you gain skill and expertise it becomes immensely satisfying. Particularly rewarding is to hear, perhaps after decades of silence, the first crackle, and then a voice in the speaker. Having achieved this major milestone, one can go on to restore the cabinet to its former glory, creating something which is both decorative, as well as functional. Your friends will be impressed!

Philip Lawson, G4FCL

March 2016

Glossary

AF – Audio Frequency - defined as 20Hz-20KHz, but say 300Hz-3KHz when setting-up a signal generator for test purposes

AM – Amplitude Modulation - the act of superimposing amplitude variations on a carrier

Bias – the voltage or current that sets the operating point of the valve or other device

Condenser – the old name for a capacitor

Trimmer – a compressed-flat, small-vaned, or beehive-shaped variable capacitor which allows the resonant frequency of an RF or IF circuit to be adjusted during alignment and calibration

Dropper – an old term for a high-wattage resistor (often with several tapping points) used to reduce the mains or HT voltage. Noted for their ability to generate heat!

IF – Intermediate Frequency - typically centred around 455KHz-465KHz, 1.6MHz, or 10.7MHz. IF coils or 'transformers' are usually screened and therefore located inside tall, square metal housings or 'cans'

HT – High Tension - anything up to several hundred volts DC. For battery-valve portables: 90VDC

LO – Local Oscillator - a circuit which generates a local signal which is mixed with the incoming RF to generate the IF signal in a superheterodyne receiver

LT – Low Tension - normally refers to the valve heater supply. Often 6.3VAC in mains AC only sets; 1.4VDC in battery-valve portables

Mains hum – the sound of 50Hz from the mains heard through the speaker

Multimeter – A tester for measuring voltage, current, and resistance. It may have a moving-coil meter (good for observing fluctuations), or a digital display (better for accuracy). The latter might also measure parameters such as inductance, capacitance, frequency, and temperature.

Pi-filter – A large series inductance (or 'choke') with a big electrolytic capacitor to ground on each end that takes 'raw' DC and converts it to 'smooth' DC. The circuit schematic looks like the Greek letter 'pi'

RCD – Residual Current Device - a mains safety device that initiates a fast disconnect if it detects an imbalance in the mains conductor currents.

Rectifier – A diode (valve or semiconductor) that converts AC to 'raw' DC and usually feeds the 'pi' filter

RF – Radio Frequency - strictly 3KHz-300GHz, but say 150KHz-150MHz in the context of old radios

Rotor – the moving part of a tuning condenser - a set of semi-circular or elliptical, closely-spaced vanes; or the moving-wafer and its associated contacts on a rotary switch

Signal generator – provides a signal at AF or RF to inject for test purposes. The RF signal can usually be amplitude modulated at AF if required

Stator – the fixed vanes of a tuning condenser which the rotor vanes move into and out of, or the fixed wafer and contacts on a rotary switch

Superhet – the superheterodyne method by which the received signal is mixed (hetrodyned) with a local oscillator to produce an IF signal

An Example Radio Restoration Project   1

LET'S LOOK at what's was involved in restoring one particular old radio set from start to finish. It should give you a rough insight into the process or methodology used, what is involved, and the issues that needed to be tackled. By extrapolation, you can imagine what may lie ahead if you decide to embark upon restoring your own set. To help you further, occasional references are made to later chapters in the form of (*Chap a.b*) so that you can explore the topic in much greater detail if desired. These later chapters deal with important matters such as safety, as well as covering a wide range of techniques for addressing the many different issues that you are likely to come across. So to our example of what you might come up against...

1.1 What Have We Got? – Let's Take a Good Look

Consider the Pye 906 "International" in **Fig 1.1**. As received, the Pye 906 is a heavy, 'table-top' model, with a wooden cabinet. It's an impressive-looking set, with its large glass dial (thankfully intact) and a multitude of buttons and knobs. Physically, it looks

Fig 1.1: *The Pye 906 "International" before restoration work starts*

in reasonable condition, with the company's "rising sun" logo still visible on top (**Fig 1.2**), cardboard back intact, and original mains lead. However; it's dusty; the cabinet is quite 'flat' (from being bleached by sunlight over the years); some of the push-buttons are very grimy and do not operate properly, and the cursor doesn't move freely.

Fig 1.2: The Pye Company's famous 'Rising Sun' logo

As the electrical condition of this set is unknown, the very first thing to do is put away any notion on plugging it in to see whether it works; powering it up at this stage can not only cause all manner of internal damage but is potentially dangerous (*Chap 4.1*). Inspecting the mains cable reveals it to be a very old cotton-covered type, whose inners are made of rubber, which hardens and becomes brittle with age. The best thing to do, is to cut it off to curb the temptation to test and because a new mains lead needs to be fitted later anyway. Locating the

Fig 1.3: A first peek inside the back - not too bad!

circuit diagram via the internet, shows that this set was released for sale in July 1939 (just before the outbreak of WWII), and is a 5-valve, 8-band superhet design for AC mains only. This last point is actually very important and has safety implications. The circuit diagram confirms that this is indeed an AC only set and uses a mains isolation transformer, and is not an AC/DC set. This influences how we eventually attach a replacement mains lead (*Chap 6.5*).

At this stage, we need to find a suitable receptacle (such as a jar, or a small freezer-bag) in which to store all of the removed bits lest they go missing. We are now in a position to have a good look inside the set. Undoing the retaining screws in the cardboard back, and removing it, reveals a pleasant surprise - an interior in relatively good condition,

Fig 1.4: *Chassis top showing the 3-gang tuning condenser (left), blackened bulbs behind the tuning dual (centre), and mains rectifier valve (right).*

Fig 1.5: *Front chassis view of the large glass tuning dial with its eight vertical tuning bars and wave-band indicator lamps (two of which are missing) below.*

Fig 1.7: *A dirt-encrusted tuning mechanism has overcome the simple cord-on-spindle friction used to drive it round.*

Fig 1.6: *Translucent amber push-buttons are a pleasing detail on this set.*

Fig 1.8: *Perished wires on the mains transformer.*

Fig 1.9: *The chaotic scene underneath the chassis. Note the heavy flywheel which (when working) endows the tuning mechanism with 'body' and momentum, and makes turning the tuning knob a much more pleasant experience.*

with nothing obviously missing, albeit there is a superficial layer of cobwebs, dirt, and the odd dead insect, and a few fraying wires (**Fig 1.3**) - all par for the course! First though, we clean the inside of the dusty back with a dust-pan and brush, and the outside with a rag and a drop of household cleaner, before putting the back to one side until the restoration is nearly finished.

To withdraw the chassis for a better look, the three Bakelite knobs (Volume, Tone, and Tuning) must be removed by slightly undoing the set-screw in each, after which the chunky chassis retaining bolts and their cup washers can be released by going underneath the cabinet and removing them. This is a heavy set, and manoeuvring it over the table to get at the screws underneath requires some care to avoid injuring oneself (*Chap 4.3*). Once done, the chassis can be drawn out - but only so far initially, because it's restrained by a length of speaker cable. Disconnecting this umbilical lead, the chassis can be taken out for inspection and the cabinet put to one side.

With the chassis on the workbench we can see immediately that the dial illumination bulbs are blackened, and even if they do work, should be replaced (**Fig 1.4**). Meanwhile, at the front, we notice that two of the three waveband indicator lamps are missing (**Fig 1.5**), and there is a row of interesting amber-resin push-buttons that need a good clean (**Fig 1.6**). The tuning mechanism, including its dial cord, appears intact, but it's covered in dirt, and when the tuning spindle is rotated, the mechanism is stiff and rough and the dial cursor largely fails to move in sympathy (**Fig 1.7**). More seriously, we observe that some wires, such as those attached to the mains transformer, are perished, the rubber insulation having gone brittle and flaked off with heating and age (**Fig 1.8**).

Turning the chassis over, we discover a veritable birds-nest of components, including a couple of modern electrolytic capacitors, which indicate that the set has been serviced at some point in recent years (**Fig 1.9**).

1.2 Beginning Restoration Work

Using a vacuum cleaner with a corner attachment and a soft 1/2" brush, we first remove surface dust and debris from the chassis (*Chap 4.4*).

At this stage we decide what needs to be replaced. Given that the intention is to restore as opposed to rebuild, the aim is to replace only that which needs to be replaced for safety and operational reasons, and no more. This not only saves time and effort, but more importantly keeps the set in as original condition as possible (*Chap 4.5*). What to do next, and techniques to be applied, are described in considerable detail later; but here is a summary of what was needed in this particular case:

Chassis Hardware Maintenance (*Chap 5*)

- Dial and Indicator Lamps: All bases cleaned and a full set of new 6V/0.5A bulbs fitted.
- Valves: All tested as satisfactory on a Taylor 45C valve tester. Cleaned (along with their bases) and put back.
- Tuning Dial: With extreme care, this large glass dial was removed, cleaned and replaced.
- Tuning mechanism (including condenser bearings and pulleys): cleaned and oiled to run freely.
- Volume, Tone, and Wave-change controls: switch cleaner applied to electrical contacts and the mechanism oiled.

Electrical Repairs (*Chap 6*)

- Resistors: None appear to be burnt from excess current which is good news. Those carrying significant current, checked, and found to be within tolerance.
- Capacitors: Electrolytic types (mostly high volt-

Fig 1.10: Bulbs and valve heaters all lit – a good start!

age and used for HT smoothing) replaced as a matter of course. Inter-stage coupling (grid block) capacitors also replaced due to loss of DC isolation.

- Internal wiring: old HT routing wires around the transformer and underneath, replaced, as were frayed speaker leads.

- Mains Cable: Original 2-core cable replaced by a modern 3-core cable and a 3-pin plug fitted with a 1 Amp fuse. Crucially, because this type of set employs a mains isolation transformer, and not an auto-transformer, the chassis can be safely earthed and earthed for safety.

Fig 1.11: *The large and rather beautiful 8-band dial*

Fig 1.12: *A break in the fine wire of this coil signals a delicate repair job*

1.3 Does It Work?

Having temporarily reconnected the speaker, we now 'clear the deck', putting stoppers on any solvent bottles, and removing these items, along with aerosols, flammable materials, and any unnecessary tools, away from the set.

At this point one must take time to think carefully, and to think ahead. In addition to many general safety issues (*Chap. 2*), there are some very serious specific hazards to consider, and some important personal safety measures to take, as we move to power-up the set (*Chap 7.1*). These measures and hazards include (but are not limited to):

- RCD protection - for protection against unexpected currents, and their potential secondary effects (such as fire and electrical shock)

- Observing the 'one hand rule' - to limit the effects of any electrical shock
- Using insulated probes - to protect from electrical shock and burns
- Wearing goggles - to protect against exploding capacitors

With these measures in place, and observing 'the 4s's' (*Chap 7.2*), switch-on of the set was uneventful. Bulbs were lit, valve heaters glowed a reassuring red, and there was a quite hum from the speaker (**Fig 1.10**). No signs of burning, no resistors glowing red, no arcing noises, and no strong smells, but no voices or music either!

This is often the case, but having paid diligent attention to the key elements mentioned earlier (valve condition, renewing electrolytic capacitors, wiring, etc.), the set ought to be very close to working. However, there is often some unique problem that needs attention. This is where fault-finding kicks in (*Chap 7.3*). Checking the HT and bias voltages revealed nothing amiss, but by pressing some of the waveband-select buttons and sending the cursor of the newly-restored tuning mechanism gliding up the dial, the set burst into life (**Fig 1.11**). Why?

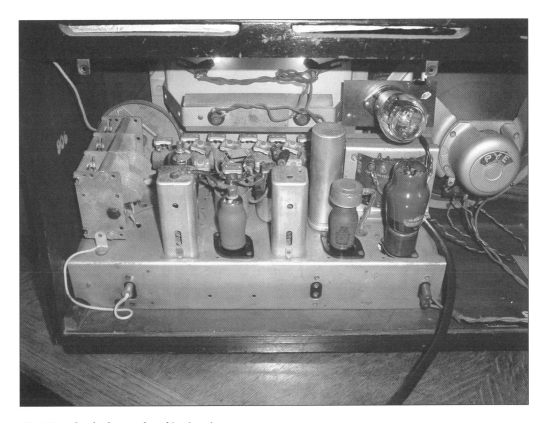

Fig 1.13: A lovely clean and working interior

A feature of this particular set is the unusually large number of RF tuning coils, trimming capacitors, and press-switches. It arises because the set has eight wavebands rather than the usual two or three, and in addition, it has four pre-set frequencies to supplement manual tuning. This leads to an arrangement that is mechanically and electrically quite complex, delicate (in the sense that there are a lot of fine wires that are easily broken), and in the case of the press-switches, a part that is difficult to access for repair and maintenance. A break was found on one of the coils, a type of fault that is seen occasionally on RF and IF coils as a result of excess current, corrosion, or perhaps accidental physical interference (**Fig 1.12**). Once the coil was repaired, and switch-cleaner worked into some intermittent pre-set controls, all was well.

However, although working, this is not the end of the matter. For a professional job, we ought to check the alignment and calibration. This means making sure that the gain-frequency response of the RF and IF circuits is correct 'the alignment' and that the wavelength indicated by the dial cursor is the same wavelength that the receiver is actually listening to 'the calibration' (*Chap 7.4*). As indicated earlier, the Pye 906 International is a complicated set because of all the different wavebands and pre-sets, so for this exercise the circuit diagram is most definitely needed. Using an AM modulated signal generator, the circuit notes explain where in the circuit to inject a signal; the frequency and level to apply; and which coils, cores, and trimmers to adjust, and in what order. For this set, the task is lengthy and the notes must be followed carefully. If you have a much simpler set, its response and calibration can often be roughly checked and adjusted by tuning-in broadcast stations of known frequency, which will save time and effort.

Having completed the electronics restoration and created a nice, working, sensitive, and calibrated receiver, the next task is to restore the cabinet.

1.4 Restoring the Cabinet

There are three major types of cabinet that the restorer will encounter, namely: wood, Bakelite and plastic (*Chap 8*). Like most pre-war sets, the Pye 906 has a really solid, heavy cabinet made of wood. Happily, this set showed no sign of flight-holes (a characteristic of woodworm infestation), so after removing dust from inside using a brush and a vacuum cleaner and finishing-off with a rag, we can proceed to tackle the exterior.

To help bring the cabinet back to something approaching its former glory, there is a wonderful solution that you can make or buy, called a 'reviving mixture' (*Chap 8.4*). Simply applying this all over with a rag will usually bring about a remarkable transformation, as it cleans and nourishes the wood, turning a dusty sun-bleached surface into a clean, deeper-coloured, rich, shiny surface. When dry, the cabinet can waxed in the

Fig 1.14: *The finished item – a splendid piece of heritage furniture*

usual way for a high finish. If there is damage to the surface, a range of techniques can be used, from filler and scratch remover, to wax crayons, which can potentially make it much less conspicuous, although it may require some time and experimentation to achieve the best result. In our example, only reviver and a little wax crayon work was needed to deliver a pleasing finish.

1.5 The Finished Item

The final task is to put the restored chassis back into the restored cabinet and to refit the back and knobs. Hopefully there will be nothing left in the bits jar afterwards that one has forgot to attach!

If we look in the back and from the front (**Figs 1.13 & 1.14**) and compare what we see now with what we had at the start (**Figs 1.1 & 1.3**) we notice quite a difference; and for the better. It has not been a quick or easy project, but we now have a beautiful piece of domestic furniture, a working piece of English radio heritage, and something that we can enjoy, not only with our eyes, but with our ears also!

This has been a quick overview of the real-life restoration of one old radio set from start to finish. What we do now, is to expand on the detailed skills and techniques that the radio restorer will need to tackle a wide range of sets. We must begin though, with salutary consideration of the many safety hazards that will arise and how to reduce the risks involved.

Safety Matters

IF YOU are thinking of undertaking a restoration, please consider this before continuing: the restoration process contains many hazards which include (but are not limited to):

- Receiving a fatal shock

- Being cut by sharp metal projections from the chassis or glass edges

- Being struck and injured by a heavy cabinet or chassis

- Being blinded by an exploding component (such as a capacitor)

- Getting accidentally burnt on a hot resistor or soldering iron

- Fire and fumes caused by overheating or shorting components

- Fire caused by accidental ignition of flammable cleaning materials

- Fire from spontaneous combustion of rags soaked with oils used for cabinet restoration

- Incapacity arising from breathing vapours from volatile liquids

- Short or long term illness caused by breathing or absorbing restoration chemicals

- Exposure to white asbestos (present in some sets) and potentially asbestosis

I cannot stress strongly enough, the need to have safety uppermost in your mind. For your own and other people's safety, you **must** consider the risks *and take steps to mitigate them.*

As we proceed through the process of restoration, particular hazards will be highlighted as a matter of course, along with suggestions as to what you can do to reduce the risk. However *you must review carefully what all the risks are in your own situation* and do everything you can to make your working environment as safe as possible. If you are in a family environment, you need to consider whether embarking upon a restoration is actually a feasible proposition, and if you were to, what additional measures you might need to put in place to keep the family safe. To help you deal with the issue of safety, here is some basic practical advice to start you off:

2.1 General Precautions

Most readers will not have access to professional facilities that are strictly controlled by company rules and employee legislation. Instead, the reader will probably be working on something akin to the kitchen table or perhaps the luxury of a shed-workshop. So:

- Keep the working area tidy, obstacle-free, well ventilated, and well-lit

- Do not have any more test equipment and materials out than is immediately necessary.

- Keep chemicals stored away from the working area (ideally in a special-purpose chemical cabinet). If they are on the bench, only remove the top/stopper when needed to dispense the contents and firmly replaced at all other times.

- Think ahead before you touch anything and don't work on live equipment if you're tired.

2.2 Electrical Shock

People have been electrocuted by contact with potentials as low as 35 Volts. The peak AC mains voltage in the UK is ten times that. The worse scenario is with AC current flowing through the heart from one hand to the other (the most likely scenario if you touch a live circuit). To make matters worse, if you grab the connection, the hand muscles tend to contract, increasing the current and making the effect far worse. So to protect yourself and others:

- Fit RCDs to you mains sockets (these will trip above a certain leakage current).

- Use a neon mains-test screwdriver to check that the chassis, and exposed metal parts are not 'mains live'.

- Use a multi-meter with well-insulated probes to check circuit voltage levels.

- Only touch live equipment with one hand at any time (to avoid current across the heart).

- Remember capacitors store charge, and you can get a nasty shock long after the equipment is disconnected.

2.3 Physical Injury

- Wear a sturdy glove(s) to avoid being cut by a heavy cabinet, a sharp chassis or glass edges.

- Think carefully about how you're going to manoeuvre that heavy cabinet and/or chassis before you pick it up! Enlist help to share the weight and make the job easier.

- Wear goggles to avoid being blinded by an exploding component (such as a capacitor).

- Only power the soldering iron when you want to use it – this is to avoid burns by accidental contact with the hot end, or the sudden ignition of volatile chemicals.

- Don't touch components such as high-wattage resistors and valves which can burn – use an infra-red thermometer to remotely check their temperature.

2.4 Fire

- Have a fire extinguisher to hand (one compatible with electrical and chemical hazards)

- Be on constant look out for overheating or shorting components. These can ignite solvents and nearby flammable materials like newspaper or cleaning rags.

- Keep tops/stoppers on all bottles – many restoration chemicals will contain flammable liquids. These are easily ignited by spillage (or even vapour alone) and heat or spark.

- Keeps rags soaked with oils used for cabinet restoration in a sealed metal tin to avoid spontaneous combustion. Lay them out flat in the garden later to dry out.

2.5 Incapacity/Illness

- Ensure there is plenty of ventilation (ie do not work in a small stuffy room) because breathing vapours from volatile liquids can cause drowsiness, nausea, and incapacity.

- Try to avoid breathing-in, or contact with, restoration chemicals, to minimise the risk of a reaction, or contracting a long term-effect such as cancer.

- Clearly label bottles of home-made mixtures (such as reviving solution) with their contents and a warning 'Poison' in large red letters to avoid them being mistaken for foodstuff.

- If you come across white asbestos, for example around mains droppers, do not touch it and do not disturb it, to avoid exposure to the risk of asbestosis.

2.6 Restored Equipment

- Ensure that metal areas cannot be touched by anyone, especially 'little fingers'

- Know the importance safety difference between 'AC Only' and 'AC/DC' sets –

'AC Only' sets may be earthed (but not always!); 'AC/DC' sets must not. This is discussed in detail later.

- Fit modern a mains cable of adequate rating and a 3-pin plug.
- Fit the lowest reasonable fuse rating – usually 1Amp.
- Check that no components are overheating

What You Need to do the Job $\quad$ **3**

H AVING CONSIDERED the risks and rewards of the undertaking, let's have a look at some of the tools, facilities, etcetera, that you might need to do the job. There's no definitive answer to cover the infinite range of tasks that you may be faced with, but the more you have from the following, the easy and quicker the restoration will be:

3.1 Facilities

- A sturdy non-conductive table or workbench.
- A non-slip surface to walk around the work area - you can't do chassis and cabinet restoration sitting down!
- Good bright lighting, from overhead fluorescent lights and/or an angle poise lamp. If you use the latter, it *must* be LED (not incandescent) or your hand and wrists will rapidly suffer from painful heat-stroke.
- Plenty of ventilation for when using solvents.
- Mains supply with RCD protection.
- A handicraft apron is useful for work on the cabinet, as it not only protect one's clothes while rubbing or cleaning bits, but it has useful pockets for tools to save your legs.
- Keep a large cake tin or similar for rags damp with solvent. Be aware that *some oils used to restore wood have the potential to spontaneously combust*, so keep rags which have been in contact with such liquids in such a tin with the lid sealed down when working to prevent ignition. You can dry them out later by fully outstretching them flat outside in the garden.
- Use a large jar to temporarily keep bits in that you remove (screws, washers, knobs, that sort of thing). Freezer bags, especially clear and re-sealable types, can be particularly useful.
- Ideally, access to a buffing wheel (for polishing knobs etc) and a grindstone for sharpening hand tools.
- A pair of goggles is handy for when machine-buffing parts and when you're unsure how electrolytic capacitors are going to react when you put the power on.
- A camera is a very useful item as you can record progress. It can provide a remarkable record of how the set used to look and the work you've put in.

3.2 Tools

Your father probably said at some point: 'you can never have enough tools'. He was right, but you can't have everything and the one that you want is usually the one that you haven't got or can't find. For what it's worth, here is my selection:

A diverse range of flat, cross-head, and jewellers screwdrivers; long, short, and angled-nose pliers; bradawl; small table/bench vice; brushes large and small from soft to stiff, from corner to bottle type; IR thermometer; croc-clips; wire-snips; wire strippers; scalpel with round and straight blades; scissors; pens; marker pens; pencils; vernier callipers (with inside & outside capability); fibre brush; penknife; Stanley knife; centre punch; tweezers (metal and plastic); monkey wrench; spanners; small brass and steel wire brushes; round and flat files; magnifying glass (hand and desk-top types); soldering irons (10 and 25W); steel rule; steel tape-measure; magnetic picker-upper; inspection mirror; small hand-torch; cyclists head-torch; feeler gauges; small electric drill/driver; paint brushes (artists; and ½" & 1" brushes to remove dust); ultra-sonic bath; range of twist drills and counter-sink; solder-sucker; a few small syringes (one each for applying lubricating oil, penetrating oil, and Vaseline); and a medium hammer.

3.3 Materials

Replacement speaker cloths and grills; lacing cord; electrical tape; wood glue; superglue; araldite; thread-lock; freezer spray; cable ties; emery paper; wire wool; washing-up liquid; scratch remover; double-sided tape; 60/40 Sn/Pb solder; tin of flux; solder wick; coloured wax sticks; a range of stains, waxes, oils and varnishes for wood; mini-tins of enamel paints as required. Polish for wood, plastic, and metal.

3.4 Parts

As required: capacitors, resistors, valves, transistors, diodes, switches, controls, knobs, terminals, screws, connectors, coloured wiring, screened cable, mains cable, and fuses (1, 3, 5, 13A).

3.5 Test equipment

Multi-meter, DVM (ideally with capacitance and inductance measurement capability), neon mains-test screwdriver, RF/AF signal generator, oscilloscope, and ideally, a valve tester.

Fig 3.1: *My trusty toolbag (front)*

3.6 Cleaning Equipment

Strong mains vacuum cleaner, plastic polish, polishing paste, Iso-Propyl Alcohol ('IPA'; **but not Beer!**), acetone, water, air-duster, rubber gloves, dusters, chamois leather, methylated spirit, white spirit, linseed oil, glass cleaner, switch cleaner, anti-static foam cleaner, silk gloves, thick gloves (for broken glass), cotton buds, wipes.

Fig 3.2: *My trusty toolbag (back)*

Beginning the Restoration Process | 4

ALTHOUGH EACH SET presents its own challenges, there is a common methodology to the restoration process which can be applied to most sets. **Table 4.1** shows a 'route map' of the various steps and a preferred 'batting order so that the process proceeds logically and efficiently. We shall use a Murphy model A70 from the late 1930s as an underlying example restoration and some other models to help illustrate the various steps in the route map from start to finish. We shall also highlight important safety points, and numerous tips to make the job easier.

4.1 Stop! Put that Plug Down

Contrary to your natural instincts, you **must** resist the temptation to plug an old set in to try it. There is nothing to be gained, as faults will be caught and corrected by the restoration process *before* they have chance to cause damage. An old neglected set almost

Assess the external condition of the set – including mains cable and plug
↓
Withdraw and survey the chassis
↓
Remove loose dirt
↓
Clean and Restore chassis hardware (lamps, dials, drives, controls etc)
↓
Electrical Repairs (resistors, capacitors, valves, wiring, mains cable etc)
↓
Electrical Test
↓
Fault-Finding and Repair
↓
Alignment and Calibration
↓
Cabinet Restoration (Wood, Bakelite or Plastic)
↓
Re-assembly
↓
Long-term care and maintenance

Table 4.1: shows a 'route map' of the various steps

Fig 4.1: Trouble waiting to happen - a perished lead to a valve top cap shorting to ground can lead to unwelcome excitement

certainly won't work, not least because the electrolytic capacitors around the smoothing choke will have deteriorated. Applying mains power at this stage can have all manner of unintended consequences, including damaging the valves if the grid-blocking capacitors have lost their isolation, or arcing if an HT cable has perished and the bare wire happens to be leaning against an IF can (**Fig 4.1**).

Far worse, unbeknown to you at this stage, if the mains cable has perished and the wires touch, as in this incredibly dangerous example (**Fig 4.2**), there is likely to be a very loud flash-bang when you plug-in, which will really grab your attention, and also the attention of your local mains trip or fuse.

So for all these reasons, trying the set first is best avoided. **Do not plug in**. The rule is: <u>Restore first – test later!</u>

Fig 4.2: *Danger in your hands – a short in the mains plug*

Fig 4.3: *Looking forlorn; dial and electrics not working*

4.2 Record What You See

As part of your initial survey and assessment of the set, grab a camera or smartphone, and take photographs of the set before you start, because there is nothing worse than not having a record of what the set looked like before you started work on it. Take some more snaps as you progress. All being well, you will be able to compare the restored product with your initial shots and be surprised at how much of a difference you've made.

4.3 Removing the Chassis from its Cabinet

To progress, the chassis has to be separated from its cabinet. Remove each knob from the front and/or side of the set by undoing its retaining screw and pulling it free. If it doesn't have a screw, it may well be held on by a semi-circular spring clip on the inside of the knob; simply pull forward, but beware that rust may increase the resistance, in which case you will

Fig 4.4: *The back intact*

Fig 4.5: The bits jar

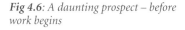

Fig 4.6: A daunting prospect – before work begins

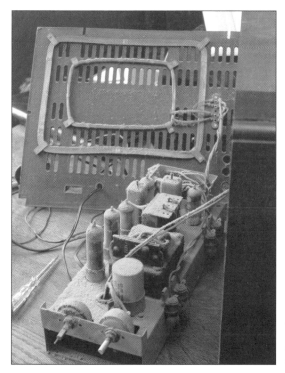

need to very carefully work a screwdriver against the cabinet in order to lever the knob off the spindle, perhaps adding a few drops of penetrating (easing oil) to encourage the process. Use a duster or a piece of thin plastic to help protect the cabinet if you need to do this.

Remove the screws and washers that hold the back, and put to one side in a jar, along with the knobs and any cloth spacers (used to stop knobs rubbing on the cabinet) that you come across. Note any items missing that ought to be replaced.

Fig 4.7: An Ekco A11 'Connoisseur' chassis with two umbilical links: one to the speaker in the cabinet and the other to a frame aerial and sockets mounted on the back cover

Just taking the back off the set to reveal what's inside can be a real revelation as **Fig 4.6** shows. Full of cobwebs and dead insects, it is (believe it or not) fairly typical of what you could be faced with. Well worth stopping for a photo!

Keeping the set as upright as possible, release the chassis retaining screws from underneath to free the chassis and add these screws, along with their washers, into your jar of bits.

Fig 4.8: Speaker and frame aerial still connected but both now free of the cabinet

If the set has a cabinet-mounted speaker (and any other appendages, such as a frame aerial and external sockets mounted on a small paxolin board for aerial, earth, gram, external speaker etc) you may have several choices. The easiest, and probably the best way if you haven't done this before, is to cut the wires close to their solder joints at the cabinet end. Better still, unsolder them (to avoid losing lead length), or ideally, un-

screw the item so it is free and can be brought out with the chassis. Particularly for big wooden-cabinet sets this last option is easier said than done as the speaker may be heavy and unwieldy, and difficult to position loosely but safely while the whole is withdrawn from the cabinet, risking damage to the speaker cone. However, the speaker will have to come out of its cabinet at some point, and releasing its umbilical now, with its leads intact, will save time if it's feasible to do so. This will be your call, bearing in mind that a chassis projection (or your finger) will

Fig 4.9: A large but delicate speaker from a floor-standing Murphy A146C

puncture the speaker cone quite easily (**Fig 4.10**).

Do bear in mind also, that with constant handling during the restoration, the umbilical wires will invariably be subject to some twisting, leading to possible fatigue and damage. This will necessitate stripping back a bit of the connecting wire, and reconnecting it, taking care to first remove the old wire from the solder-tag while not overheating the joint.

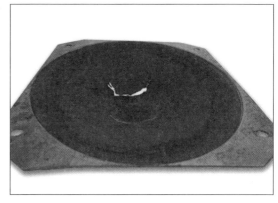

Fig 4.10: *What can go wrong if handled incorrectly*

Safety point: Remember that you will be manoeuvring two very heavy and awkward-to-control items, probably in a domestic space, where things can topple and get damaged. Even worse, you or a bystander can be injured by an ill-judged manoeuvre resulting in a bash from a heavy cabinet or

Fig 4.11: *Chassis out of the cabinet*

a cut from one of the many sharp features of the chassis. Whatever your age and agility (or lack of it) **think carefully** about what you are doing and **take your time**. Use this reminder:

Look – what can I see?

Think – what could happen; what are my options?

Do – select the best method

The key is to stop, or take your time, to avoid doing something that you may regret. This is also excellent advice for when we get around to removing fragile glass tuning dials!

4.4 Loose Dirt Removal

Having drawn the chassis out, put its cabinet, back, and speaker (if applicable), to one side. Grab the vacuum cleaner, fit the corner attachment, and go all round the chassis, on top and underneath, using a small brush to generally loosen dirt so that the vacuum can pick up as much dust and debris as possible from all the nooks and crannies and open surfaces. This debris may include a wide variety of tiny, but expired creatures, who made the set their home! Repeat for the back and cabinet. Be careful you do the speaker cone – it might be safer to use the brush attachment and a lower suction, or to clean it manually outside with a soft brush and blowing the dirt away with plenty of puff. You should end-up with something like this which is cleaner, but still has hard-on dirt that we shall remove in due course.

Fig 4.12: A view of wildlife activities underneath

A salutary point to make here is that you will spend a lot of time cleaning things during the restoration and it can be hard and mucky graft!

4.5 Restoration vs Rebuild

Once the cabinet and chassis are separated and roughly cleaned, all manner of issues are likely to become apparent. A practical and ethical point is that we are about to embark upon a restoration *not* a rebuild. The plan is *not* to replace everything in sight, but to change only that which needs changing and to provide some belated maintenance. If a component is removed, the set loses a little of its originality. That said, some components (such as electrolytic capacitors) will almost certainly need to be replaced by modern components to get the set into working condition, and some items (like mains leads) will often require replacement for reasons of safety. As to the rest, the trick is to know which components will last and which could potentially fail in the future and replace those too. This assessment of risk of electrical failure versus keeping a component for originality is especially difficult for the less experienced, who understandably may want to err on the side of caution and initiate a replacement. Where a replacement capacitor is fitted (for example), some restorers will, where feasible, hide it within the shell of the original, to help maintain authenticity.

Fig 4.13: *A Bush DAC90A after the initial vacuum clean*

Fig 4.14: A plethora of items to be examined- including the dial cord, switches, controls, and a range of components

One should also remember that as the vast majority of valves are no longer manufactured, each time a valve is removed and thrown away, the pool of valves is diminished. This is a potentially serious problem for the restorer as it makes valves harder to find. A typical ethical issue could be whether a special valve such as a 'Magic Eye', often used as a tuning indicator, really needs to be replaced just because it is a bit dimmer than one would like. For the greater good, it might be best to keep it in circulation and avoid replacing it for as long as possible.

A further issue is how to deal with wooden cabinets. Ideally these should be restored using the techniques described later. However, some would completely strip the cabinet and start again. This is a radical measure and one could argue that it degrades the authenticity of the set, but it is an option and can provide an attractive, contemporary alternative.

Chassis Hardware: Maintenance

T HIS STAGE is really about cleaning and oiling and various mechanical repairs. You may need to remove corrosion from the tuning condenser, and perhaps straighten its rotor if it catches the stator. An important, and I think, rather nice job, is to clean, oil, and grease, the tuning mechanism's bearings and pulleys so that the tuning knob rotates majestically and freely without the roughness of dry or seized bearings. You might need to put in a new dial cord if it uses one, change the odd dial bulb if blown and replace any 'bodges' made by previous owners or service personnel. Switches and controls will also need cleaning and lubricating – more of that later.

Perhaps the most risky thing that you will have to do at this stage is to remove, clean and reinstate the tuning dial. Invariably, the glass is held on to the chassis or cabinet with metal clips with a rubber cushion between it and the glass. With age, the rubber hardens so that the glass, rubber, and clip become one. We will discuss the detail of

Fig 5.1: *Removing the glass Tuning Dial – be afraid, very afraid!*

how to tackle this later, but suffice to say that there are three obvious dangers: applying too much pressure causing the glass to break; letting it slip from your hands while cleaning it (which generally has the same effect!), and running your hand over a sharp edge in the glass, possibly necessitating a trip to the medical cabinet or your favourite A&E department. This task is a real adrenalin-rush and if you mess it up it will probably be a show-stopper. Yes you might be able to find another set with a dial you can salvage, or yes, even make a new one, but you really, don't want to go through that agony. We will discuss at length how to best tackle the task in order to reduce the risk to you and the glass dial.

5.1 Dial Lamps

Locate the dial lamps which are usually held via a screw or bayonet fitting. These normally come out easily, but remember to try and twist the metal base rather than the glass bulb, or you may find that you are left with the bulb in your fingers and the base in the holder. In the latter event, or in extremis - if the lamp is generally seized, you may need to run a drop of penetrating

Fig 5.2: *Blackened bulbs ripe for replacement*

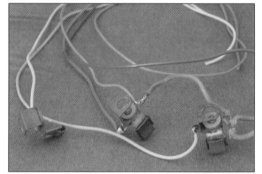

Fig 5.3: *Typical bulb holders; some wiring replaced*

(easing) oil down between the base and the holder to free it and to use a pair of pliers to help twist it free. A fiddly exercise, but the two should eventually separate. Once released, test the bulb for continuity with a multi-meter on a low resistance range. If it passes, clean the metal body and centre contact with a small piece of emery paper and clean the bulb proper with a cloth laced with a drop of glass-cleaner or with dilute soapy water and dry-off. Put to one side for later, otherwise, or if the bulb is black, discard, make a note of the shape, fitting, and any voltage/current/wattage markings, and get another one. Clean and dry-off the inside of the lamp holder with emery paper and IPA.

5.2 Valves

If they are large valves with a ceramic base, grab the base (not the glass bulb!) of each valve in turn, and wriggle it slightly while pulling to remove it from its holder. If they

Fig 5.4: A Cossor 6SN7GT double triode - beware accidentally rubbing the markings off

Fig 5.5: Look out for loose and flaking metallisation from this Mullard EF39 screened pentode

Fig 5.6: An 'all-glass' valve

are smaller 'all-glass' types you can grab the body with your fingers, but try to keep them off the writing on the bulb. Having got them out, inspect what you have. If the valve has only a light amount of dirt on it consider using the old trick of breathing on the glass (to deposit a slight condensation) and wiping it clean with a lint-free cloth. It works really well; but beware; the valve markings will come off easily and irretrievably at a stroke if your cloth goes over them, so be very careful indeed to go round not over them. It is easier said than done. Take your time. The same goes for the base. If there is a lot of grime, you can use a cloth laced with glass cleaner or soapy water, but again, avoid the markings. If the valve is coated with a metallization (to form an electrical screen around the bulb) the situation is a little more problematic: the bonding tends to fail with age and the metal flakes off. In this case I would gently dust the surface with a soft brush, remove any loose coating, and leave it at that. If you find that the valve bulb rotates slightly with respect to its base, then there is a simple but magic remedy: run a thin line of superglue around the top of the base where it meets the glass and you will have a solid item again within seconds. The same goes for a loose top-cap.

Fig 5.7: Cleaning valve pins

Now clean the pins on the valve base. A sharp pen-knife can be used as a rather course but traditional way to scrape-off troublesome insulating deposits and as a quick alternative to emery paper; but in either case, use a small cloth or cotton-bud dipped in IPA to clean-off the fine debris.

If you're lucky enough to have access to a valve-tester, check each valve, note its characteristics, and decide which (if any) need replacing. Valves are surprisingly resilient and can keep good for decades, but unless obviously damaged or the glass is milky coloured from vacuum failure, you cannot tell the electrical condition of a valve just by looking at it. In the absence of the valve tester, assume they are all good for now and we will revisit this issue later.

5.3 Tuning Dials

The next task is not for the faint-hearted. The tuning-dial, which could be either part of the chassis assembly or fixed to the cabinet, needs to be removed for cleaning. If you break the glass, it will ruin your day, if not your life, because you will have lost an important original item and you will have serious trouble trying to get a replacement. Take your time, and use the *Look, See, Do* principle espoused earlier. The tuning dial will normally be seated in rubber cushions between metal clips on the chassis, or held in the cabinet between a soft fabric on the cabinet side and a rubber cushion com-

Fig 5.8: A Mullard Mark IV Valve Tester

pressed by metal clip on the other. Either way, over time the rubber solidifies and the metal-rubber-glass interface becomes dry, rigid, and brittle. The challenge is to prize away the rubber, with its mount, away from the glass without breaking it, which is easier said than done, especially if you're working partially blind within the depths of the cabinet. The trick is to take your time: run some soapy water over the rubber. This may help a little, but you will need to carefully use a screwdriver blade or penknife blade to carefully and gradually ease the rubber away from the glass. I stress gradually, and you must continually think about where and how much pressure you're applying to the glass. This pressure needs to be spread as widely as practicable, not concentrated at a point, or the glass will break. Having successfully (we hope) removed all the retaining clips, be very careful not to then drop the glass dial or scrape it against the chassis.

The next step is straightforward, but not without danger to you and the dial. Keeping the dial low over a soft surface, clean both sides very gently with a soft cloth and warm soapy water. The markings should not come away, but be alert; I suggest just dab that side at first to confirm that this is the case and be aware that this wet slippery object could easily drop out of your hands - so do keep it low over a soft surface as

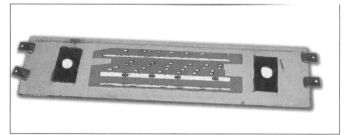

Fig 5.9: Removing a glass tuning-dial is a risky business

suggested. Also be aware of any sharp edges so that you don't cut yourself. The side of the glass which isn't printed could be cleaned instead with a commercial glass cleaner (such as that sold for car window-screens) and a lint-free cloth or chamois leather if preferred. Once cleaned by whichever method, put it to one side to dry and from then on, always handle with a new duster or silk gloves.

5.4 Chassis Clean

Now is a good time to inspect the chassis and see what needs doing. Although still looking a bit dirty after its vacuuming, it should all (or nearly all) be there. There will doubtless be some obvious problems, which could range from a broken dial cord to perished wires, and perhaps an overheated resistor, plus other faults that won't become apparent until later. For now, look to see whether there are any small mechanical components, such as rubber seats, dial cursors, or bits of the tuning assembly (such as pulleys and springs) which will dissemble easily. Put these to one side and run them through into an ultra-sonic or manual bath of warm soapy

Fig 5.10: *An ultrasonic bath is great for cleaning small objects*

water. Once clean, rinse and lay out the items on paper towels to dry. If necessary, degrease any mechanical bits (such as pulleys) with IPA.

Turning to the chassis proper, use a small wire-brush to remove any surface rust, then a rag dipped in warm soapy water as a damp cloth to gently remove grime from resistors and capacitors, dial-back-plate, tuning mechanism, controls, sockets, mains and speaker transformers etc. Be careful working near exposed coils as these have fine wires which are easily damaged and not so easily repaired. Clean the chassis itself by going in between components as best you can, and spruce-up the casings of those tall proud IF transformers. Use a dentist's mini bottle-brush to clean large valve-holder sockets and any sockets provided for aerial, earth, pickup and gram; allow the whole assembly to dry. At

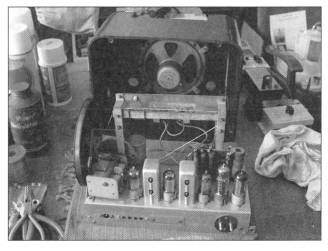

Fig 5.11: *A Bush DAC90A chassis looking resplendent after its bath*

the end of this you should have a very clean and smart-looking chassis to work with. Don't worry that you won't be able to remove the last bit of dirt from all the nooks and crannies – it's not worth the time, effort, and risk of disturbing major components just for cosmetic reasons. Now re-attach to the chassis any bits that you removed for cleaning.

Fig 5.12: The simple tuning mechanism in a 'Kent' receiver

5.5 Tuner Drive Mechanism

Over a period of time several things happen that cause the tuning mechanism to deteriorate or fail. First, the oil/grease in the tuning condenser ball-race solidifies, causing the tuning knob to feel rough when it's turned. To make matters worse, if the set has a dial cord, build-up of dirt around the pulleys and its solidification in the warm cabinet generates friction which can make the tuner stiff to operate. Ultimately, the driving friction of cord-against-steel provided by the tuning control, (often just a couple of turns of dial cord over a smooth spindle held in tension by a spring(s) on the tuning drum) becomes insufficient to overcome the friction in the pulleys and the tuning mechanism either 'stutters' or fails completely, and may result in the dial cord breaking.

Fig 5.13: Refreshing the ball-race

These problems are easily avoided by routine maintenance - which of course, never happens. Happily, you can soon correct these problems. I would say that reviving a tuning mechanism is one of the great joys of restoration and something which you can do quite quickly and easily. The first thing is to get some lubricating oil into the bearings at each end of the tuning condenser and rotate the rotor back and forth a few times. In a few minutes this should remove the rough feel to the movement and give you a beautifully smooth experience. You can apply the oil in the traditional way by putting a drop or two on screwdriver-blade, transferring it to the area concerned and letting it run in, but a far better way (which is much less hit-and-miss and quicker), is to use a small syringe kept in the toolbox for the purpose. It saves a lot of time, and I keep similar syringes for applying easing oil and Vaseline.

Next, if there is a tuning mechanism, make a very careful note of how the dial cord is strung; if there is a missing or broken cord you may need to obtain circuit diagram and refer to the accompanying notes

Fig 5.14: Touch-up the dial back-plate to add missing paint

which often have stringing information. Remove the cord to make sure the pulley centres are clean and oil them so each rotates freely. Now inspect the 'V' of each pulley, the concave guide in the control spindle, and the cord race of the tuning drum: each of these must be clean and free of dirt and grease. Using a cotton bud or wipe, apply IPA while rotating each item. Don't touch the cleaned area to avoid depositing grease from your fingers which will defeat the object. Add a drop of oil now to the drive spindle where is passes through the chassis in a collar, possibly via a 'C' retaining clip to create

Fig 5.15: The wave-change switch is frequently busy with wires and hard to access

Fig 5.16: A close-up of a single wafer rotary switch with spindle removed showing the rotary slider and radial fixed contacts

an interface film and ease rotation - but don't allow it to run down the spindle to where the dial cord is or the driving friction will be ruined. Finally, refit the springs to the drum and re-thread the dial cord, if necessary replacing it with modern lacing cord of the required diameter. Don't worry about fitting the cursor to the dial cord – that can wait until later when you have the receiver working and are ready to perform calibration. If necessary, use a touch of enamel paint to restore the dial's back-plate if flaking or corrosion has occurred. Take care to use the right shade and thickness of paint so that the repair isn't obvious.

If the tuning dial is glass, then clean it as described earlier in 'glassware clean'. However, if it is an early translucent material, take a cotton bud or small soft cloth and very gently wipe it clean. Dampen it if you need to, but take your time and be alert for possible signs of the lettering coming off. Alternatively, if the dial is Mother of Pearl (easily recognised by its

Fig 5.17: *A row of 10 push-switches for wave-changing in an RGD receiver*

lovely silvery-white finish and multi-coloured sheen), and is heavily covered in grime, clean it very gently with a slightly damp (but not wet) soft cloth. After this and for light contamination, follow the practice of some jewellers and use lemon oil applied with a silk cloth to clean, protect, and show-off the surface.

5.6 Wave-change switches

Underneath the chassis you will probably find, depending on the complexity of the receiver, a few, or perhaps a lot, of rotary wafer-switches usually driven from a central spindle or driveshaft.

The task here is to clean each the contacts with a foam (not cotton) bud soaked in IPA. This is often a fiddly task, as some contacts may be hard to get to. You will need to place the tip of the bud on the contact and turn the spindle so that all, or as much of the moving contact as you can access, is cleaned by the tip while at the same time not allowing the bud to become entangled on the sharp edges of the rotor, or the fixed stators. If there is a significant accumulation of dirt, a fibre brush can be used first to clear it away. Once clean, apply a squirt of switch cleaner, either directly, or via a 'bud to the contacts to enhance contact and movement. You should not try to adjust the springy fixed stator contacts (which may grip the rotor contacts from both sides) unless you really have to. If, in rare cases, they are too far away and don't make contact with the rotor, then one will need to apply slight a pressure to force the resting position to be closer, however, the danger is that if pushed too far, the rotor contact will hit the stator contact, bending it into a heap, from which it will be difficult, if not impossible, to recover. Contact position is very critical, so any potential modification needs to be well thought through. To finish, add a drop of oil to the shaft where it passes through the chassis wall in a collar (as with the tuning spindle above) and at the other end where the chassis grips the rotating spindle via a spring clip or other arrangement. This will help reduce friction and give a nicer mechanical switching experience. The same general advice applies to push switches, which can be more devilish to clean owing to the higher density of contacts and some wicked enclosure methods.

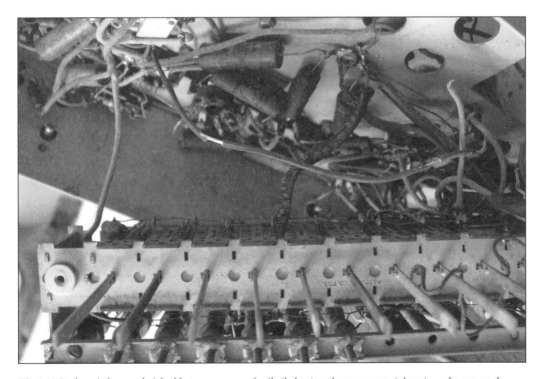

Fig 5.18 Push-switches sandwiched between a row of coils (below) and components (above) can be extremely difficult to extricate for maintenance.

Fig 5.19: *A typical volume/tone control*   *Fig 5.20*: *Lifting the retaining tabs*   *Fig 5.21*: *All four tabs pulled back*

5.7 Controls

Volume and tone controls will also need some TLC. Without attention, these will probably be 'noisy' (that is, operate intermittently) as a result of dry and accumulated dirt, and possibly lack of tension of the rotating wiper on the conductive track. These controls can often (and should) be repaired without needing to be replaced. If the control has an opening under its contact ledge or in the body, you could try squirting some switch cleaner in and rotating the control. This rather quick and course approach is often a surprisingly effective reviver, but to do the job properly, you will probably need to proceed as follows:

Unsolder and disconnect the wires to the control, undo the hexagonal retaining nut with pliers, (or preferably a spanner), and remove it. These controls usually have a ceramic top containing the spindle, track, and wiper mechanism, and either a metal surround or a metal and ceramic bottom containing a switch (for an on-off control). Use a penknife (preferably) or the blade of a small screwdriver, to lift up the metal tabs on the top, and pull-away the two halves. Now examine the condition of the wiper and track and use IPA to clean the track, and by back-and-forth movement, the wiper. If you consider that the wiper-on-track pressure is lacking, it may be possible to remove the 'C' clip, withdraw the spindle and wiper mechanism from the collar, bend the wiper down a little with pliers and reassemble, but don't do this unless you have to, as excess pressure on the track will quickly wear it out. After refitting the two halves, bend the retaining tabs back into position with a flat bladed screwdriver. Be mindful that these tabs can only be bent back and forth a few times before the metal fractures, so try and ensure that your maintenance is comprehensive (that is, you won't need to go back in) before you force the tabs back down again.

While on the subject, there is an old trick which involves running a pencil over the track to replace lost carbon. While this may not stand up to academic scrutiny be-

Fig 5.23: *Circular resistive track and rotating contact (front view)*

Fig 5.22: *Separated into switch base (left) and rotary potentiometer (right)*

cause a) you don't know what the resistivity of the carbon in the pencil is compared to what's on the track, and b) it is not clear how the 'replacement' carbon sticks to the track, nevertheless it is a well-known remedy and technique which may work for you. If it saves you having to replace a control, why not give it a try? If you do, blow off the excess carbon, and reassemble the two halves reseating the metal tabs in their rightful positions. To finish, as with the wave-change and tuning spindles, apply a drop of oil to the 'C' clip next to the collar to help promote smooth rotation.

On the subject of noisy controls, we should not forget that if any part of the rotor of the tuning condenser touches its stator, a crackle will result. Just check that the rotor moves freely and there is no apparent shorting. If there is shorting, the slit blades on the rotor can be pushed slightly to cure the problem. Shorting can be hard to spot

Fig 5.24: *Circular resistive track and rotating contact (oblique view)*

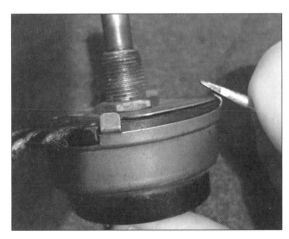

Fig 5.25: *Bending the tabs back into position after the track has been cleaned*

with narrow spacing's, awkward viewing angles, and lack of tell-tale scratches on the rotor, so recheck this point if noise is experienced while tuning when you have the set working.

Electrical Repairs

EACH SET is unique, but generally speaking, transformers, coils, low-value capacitors and resistors will be absolutely fine and can be left alone. However, depending on the set's history, you will almost certainly need to replace the mains smoothing capacitors and grid blocking capacitors, but surprisingly perhaps, valves, even ancient ones, stand the test of time very well and it is very rare that they all need replacing.

A critical action that you must undertake is to establish whether the set is 'AC Only' or 'AC/DC'. The result profoundly affects how you replace the mains lead and the relative safety of any exposed metal. This issue, and its serious safety implications, is discussed in detail later.

6.1 Resistors

Look at the resistors. Some may be a little discoloured with age and thermal cycling, but be alert to any which are obviously burnt. The latter poses two compelling questions: 'can I get another of that value and wattage'? And 'why is it burnt?' The answer to the first is almost certainly yes, even if you don't have one immediately available in your toolbox, but to answer the second and arguably more important question, you will have to go looking for clues. As you examine the chassis, do you notice any wires that are perished? If so what is their function?

6.2 Capacitors

Now look around for any electrolytic ca-

Fig 6.1: *This perished connection to a valve top-cap is touching the IF can, shorting it to ground*

Fig 6.2: *The can removed revealing the extent of the perishing*

pacitors, that is, capacitors which are normally polarised. Around the mains transformer there is often a tall cylindrical 'can' bolted to the chassis with a split circular strap. This usually contains two capacitors (perhaps marked something like '16+16uF 500V wkg') each with a contact on the top invariably marked with a coloured identification dot, often red, green, or yellow.

These contacts are connected via the wiring to the two ends of a large inductance (or choke) in a classic 'pi-filter' configuration. The opposite ends of the capacitors have a common (tied) connection which is the metal can (or case) connecting them to ground. This pi-network smooths out the rectified AC into something approaching constant DC for HT supply purposes. Because they must handle large voltages, and because their quality is hard to assess, I would usually replace these as a matter of course with modern equivalents. You will probably find several other metal electrolytic capacitors, and if it is an old set, you should replace these too. Ensure that the working voltage of your replacement capacitor is at least as high as the one that you're removing.

Contrary to what you might think, I would not replace any other capacitors (even wax ones) without good reason. Capacitors, like resistors can be measured if required with a hand-held tester with that capability. Always remember though, that the component, whether resistor, inductor or capacitor, is affected by those around it, so you may need to disconnect one end to assess its value.

At this stage then, I would regard all other capacitors as good, but I would be inclined, using the circuit diagram, to locate each grid blocking capacitor and check its DC (leakage) resistance. The purpose of the inter-stage grid blocking capacitor is to pass the RF or AF signal from one stage to the next, however in mains valve receivers this signal is commonly taken from the anode of one stage (which is at HT - up to several hundred volts) and delivered to the grid of the next stage. This is fine so long as the capacitor's DC isolation is good and it prevents (blocks) the DC from getting through.

Fig 6.3: Perished connections to a mains transformer which need to be replaced

Fig 6.4: Perished connections to a mains dropper which also need to be replaced

Unfortunately, the resistance of this capacitor may deteriorate with age and the inter-stage DC isolation fails. The result is that the negative bias voltage on the grid of the next stage is pulled positive causing the valve to draw more anode current, changing the operating point, generating electrical noise, and perhaps more to the point, causing

Fig 6.5: *A 4-capacitor chassis mount electrolytic for HT smoothing*

Fig 6.6: *Colour coded contacts identify each capacitor*

damage to the valve and associated resistors by excessive heat dissipation. Quite how much deterioration in the DC resistance of the capacitor can be tolerated depends on a number of factors, but as a rule, I would be worried if I found it had dropped from (effectively) infinity when new, down to say 10 mega-ohm. This may still sound a high resistance, but the grid is an extremely sensitive high-impedance input, and subject to the value of any grid leak resistor, the resulting current can generate a revised grid bias that when multiplied by the valve's trans-conductance can have a significant impact on its anode current. If in doubt, change for a modern component of similar capacitance and a voltage-rating at least as high as the original.

Safety Point: Remember capacitors store charge, and you can get a nasty shock long after the equipment is disconnected. With the set turned off, use an insulated screwdriver or wire, to short electrolytic capacitors to ground to dissipate the charge.

6.3 Valves

As to valves, replacements can usually be obtained over the Internet, but in the event of difficulty there are alter-

Fig 6.7: *Value and polarity information for each capacitance on the side of the 'can'*

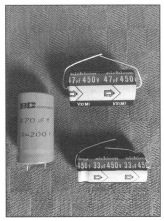

Fig 6.8: *Modern wire-ended high-voltage electrolytics suitable for HT smoothing*

native options. For example, you could replace a full or half-wave rectifier valve with modern diodes. The 1N4007 is a wire-ended solid-state rectifier diode with a 1KV repetitive reverse-breakdown voltage and can take a maximum average forward current of 1Amp [1]. Now, given that the recommended reverse-surge rating for such diodes is 1.4 times the secondary AC voltage for a full-wave rectifier, and 2.8 times the secondary AC voltage in the case of a half-wave rectifier, this component should cope

Fig 6.9: Make sure that the inter-stage grid-blocking capacitor is up to the job

easily with mains secondary of up to 700V and 350V respectively [2]. The secondary voltages in the vast majority of sets will be less than this, and as the HT current will also be well within the diode rating, this makes this particular diode-rectifier an ideal and versatile solution to the problem. To fit it, simply remove the original valve, block-off the top of the valve-holder with a plug or tape so that it cannot be used, and wire the 1N4007 between the anode and cathode pins of the valve base. Two are required for full- and one for half-wave rectification. Be very careful to observe the diode markings and fit it the correct way round - incorrect fitting may (among other things!) destroy the set's electrolytic capacitors.

It is even possible to replace a valve with a near-equivalent having a different pin-out. Here, an adapter can be made from copper wire inserts of the correct gauge fashioned to plug into the original valve base and soldered to a new valve-holder above, in which is seated the replacement valve. An example of the practice is shown in **Fig 6.10** & **Fig 6.11**.

6.4 Internal Wiring

Fig 6.1 shows a lead popping out of an IF transformer on its way to a valve top cap. With time and heat the rubber has hardened and flaked away exposing the wire. This wire carries the HT voltage via a resistor and the IF coil to the valve's anode. If it leans on the metal of the IF transformer case the high resistance path through the valve is replaced by a low resistance short; this will cause sparking, and will result either in a burnt-out winding or an overheated or burnt-out resistor. So be on the lookout for things which are amiss and be aware of

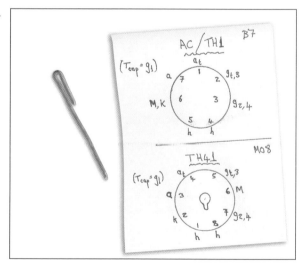

Fig 6.10: The pin-out of the chassis and adapter bases. Copper 'hairpins' are soldered under the adapter, aligned, and pushed into the original valve base in the chassis

their potential consequences – this will provide valuable clues, and 'close the loop' as to why things have happened. You may find one or two resistors look discoloured, burnt, or damaged; check their value with a DVM. Bearing in mind their tolerance (usually +/-10% or +/-20%), consider their physical condition and whether they are out of range, and if they are, replace them.

Elsewhere, check cables and cable looms generally and replace any perished cables. Likewise, take a careful look at any screened cable, especially where it is runs to a valve top-hat; these may carry a high voltage and need to be intact - look for fraying of the outer sheath and shorting to a potentially perished inner wire. Check the mains tap setting on the transformer is correct and that the connection, however made, is clean and conductive.

Fig 6.11: *The adapter pushed and seated into the original base and the replacement valve pushed into the top of the adapter.*

Inspect solder joints for brightness and remake if dull, as the joint could be 'dry'- that is oxidised, physically weak, and high-resistance. A 25W iron is much more effective when soldering older sets than a 10W iron which is more suitable to smaller, modern electronics. Although reels of traditional 60/40 tin/lead electrical solder contain flux, consider adding a dab from an external tin of flux if you are working a joint for any length of time, as flux burns-off and needs to be replaced. Remove any excess when cool using a cotton-bud dipped in IPA.

Look at the valve holders – are any of the individual pin contacts damaged? If they are, either replace the entire valve holder, or where possible, remove the broken pin contact and replace it with one salvaged from a spare holder.

6.5 Mains cable

We now turn our attention to the mains lead, which could well be a flex, whose rubber insulation becomes brittle and flaky with age. This is extremely dangerous as the slightest

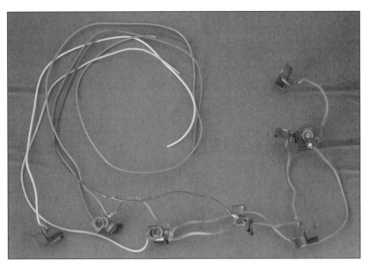

Fig 6.12: A daisy-chain of dial bulb-holders, some wiring replaced

twist of the flex may lead to a mains short-circuit, the heat of which may lead to a fire. Whatever the cable, unless it really is modern, remove it.

Caution: Some sets were made with a re-sistive mains 'dropper' lead. If the set's lead is particularly thick and has an unusually high resistance (more than a few ohms) it may well be one of these. In this case, make a note of the resistance in each of the two wires before discarding the lead. Better still; check the circuit diagram notes for any information on the expected mains-lead resistance, dissipation, and proper length, just in case it has been foreshortened. The correct total resistance at an adequate wattage will need to be added as a new component inside the set in due course to compensate for the lack of voltage drop in the new mains lead. If this component is not added, the set will be stressed by overvoltage, larger than expected currents will flow, and the set will become hotter and less safe than normal.

Now you **must** ascertain, either by looking at the notes on the back of the set, or from labels in the cabinet, or by looking at the circuit diagram and notes, whether your set is an 'AC/DC' type or 'AC only'. This is crucial, because in the next step, if you get it wrong, not only do you risk damaging the set, including causing it to overheat, but you may electrocute someone. It is that serious!

Fig 6.13: The new wiring loom to a 'magic-eye' and the original wires for comparison

Fig 6.14: New multi-coloured wiring looms in place for the illuminated wave-band indicator (left) 'magic-eye' (centre), and loudspeaker (right)

If you have an 'AC/DC' set

Replace the original 2-core mains cable with good quality 2-core mains cable of adequate current rating. <u>There is no earth wire</u> because this type of set has no mains isolation transformer which means the chassis is intentionally 'floating' and may be at either live or neutral mains potential depending on which way the live and neutral wires are presented to the mains. Electrical safety deliberately relies on the cabinet, back, knobs, and treated external screws, to insulate the user from potentially lethal voltages present on the chassis and the metal parts connected to it. In the old days, with two pin plugs, the chassis could be in either state – live or neutral.

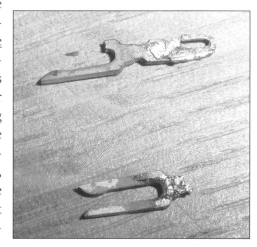

Fig 6.15: A broken pin contact extracted with pliers from a valve holder and replaced with one salvaged from a spare holder

Now however, with irreversible (three-pin) plugs we know that the blue wire is at neutral potential and so we take the opportunity to arrange the safer, 'chassis neutral' option. Hence for everyone's safety you need to do the following three things:

1   Locate the original cable connection points in the set. You should find that one is electrically connected a resistive 'mains dropper', which provides HT and LT supplies to the set, this we will make our 'live' connection point, while the other is electrically connected more or less directly, (perhaps via a bulb(s)) to the chassis; this we will make our 'neutral' connection point. You can confirm which is which with a multi-meter: our 'live' connection point will have an electrical resistance to chassis in the order of kilo-ohms, and our 'neutral' connection point will have a much lower electrical resistance to chassis, in the order of ohms.

2   Now, wire the mains plug, carefully observing the standard brown-to-live and blue-to-neutral pin convention, and confirm no connection to the earth pin. At the other end of the replacement 2-core cable, connect the brown (live) wire to our 'live' connection point, and the blue (neutral) wire to our neutral connection point.

3   Ensure that no metal parts, whether chassis, control spindles, or any other item are accessible from the outside of the set. You may find that the back and knob retaining screws are coated with beeswax or some other material to insulate them from

Fig 6.16: Roulette with a 2-pin plug: one way round is reasonably safe, the other lethal

the user. Where this is removed for the servicing and restoration activity, it should be replaced later.

Although wiring for a near neutral chassis is safer, faults can occur and so every effort should still be made to avoid the possibility of someone coming into contact with the chassis or any metal connected to it.

If you have an 'AC only' set

The vast majority of these use a mains isolation transformer, which 'separates' the mains from the chassis enabling it to be earthed for safety. Exceptionally however, you may have an 'AC only' set which does not have an isolation transformer and instead uses an auto-transformer, an AC version of the 'mains dropper' found in the AC/DC sets just described. If this is the case you must proceed as for the AC/DC set. Otherwise, which will usually be the case, proceed as follows:

Replace the original 2-core mains cable with good quality 3-core mains cable of adequate current rating. Wire the mains plug and connect the blue and brown mains wires of the replacement cable to the original cable connection points in the set – ori-

Fig 6.17: *An AC/DC set with floating chassis that must be kept away from prying fingers*

entation should not matter as they will invariably go to the two ends of a mains input isolating transformer. Connect the green/yellow wire to the chassis via a nearby, sturdy, chassis solder tag. This provides a measure of safety against fault conditions and to anyone touching the chassis. As with modern electrical equipment, leakage current to earth is picked-up by your household RCD and trips it to indicate a problem. If your mains circuit does not have RCDs, then fit one to your mains socket and plug the set into that as a safety measure.

Generally

With both types of set, fit the mains plug with the lowest current fuse that you can get away with. Allowing for some surge-current at switch-on, this fuse should be typically 1 Amp. You should also provide a new grommet where the cable leaves the assembly to prevent the chassis biting into the cable and initiating a mains-earth short.

Electrical Testing

GETTING TO this point has taken considerable effort, but cleverly, we have rectified numerous problems before they appear. If the valves are good (items which you may not have the capability to test) then there is a fighting chance that you will hear encouraging sounds at switch-on.

7.1 Preparation & Safety Measures

Personal safety and the safety of others is paramount. You need to *think ahead*. For example, if you are working on newspapers spread out to protect the surface of the table, and even worse have not put the tops back on your solvent bottles, really bad things can happen and the dangers can escalate very quickly; so: Read *Chap. 2* 'Safety Matters' before proceeding further.

'Clear the decks'. Put stoppers on any solvent bottles and move them well away before the set is powered-up. Also remove any flammable material (like newspaper and rags) that the chassis may be sitting on, and put away unnecessary tools. If you have a small fire-extinguisher, then keep it nearby - this may sound extreme, but if things are getting out of hand it's not really an academic debate.

Ensure that valves and pilot lamps have been refitted, and if you have temporarily disconnected the speaker, reconnect it. Double-check any electrolytic capacitors that you replaced are the right way round *and* are of sufficient working voltage, confirm your new mains wiring (noting the important AC vs AC/DC set distinction) is correct, and that the fuse is *not* a standard 13A but considerably lower to suit the wattage of the set.

Think carefully about what you are doing and **take your time**.

Use this reminder:

Look – what can I see?

Think – what could happen; what are my options?

Do – which the best way forward?

Safety point (RCD): If your mains outlet does not have already Residual Current Device (RCD) protection (usually, though not always, via the consumer unit or 'fuse-box'), or if you are unsure whether it does, then fit a portable approved RCD into the mains outlet that you intent to plug the set into. The RCD is a safety device which detects imbalance between the live and neutral wire currents, usually caused by an unexpected earth leakage current. It trips very quickly cutting the live voltage to provide a measure of safety against electrocution and possibly fire.

Safety point (**electrical shock & burns**): Our next challenge, in handling a live set, is to avoid electrical shock or getting burnt. If you really must touch a powered chassis or a component directly, do it lightly using the finger(s) of only *one* hand (to avoid currents through the body) while keeping the other hand free or in your pocket. Better still; don't touch anything except via the insulated probes of your multi-meter or other test equipment. If it's likely to get hot, use an infra-red thermometer to remotely check its temperature.

Safety point (**electrolytic capacitors**): A good school-friend of mine once misinterpreted the polarity marking and put an electrolytic in 'back to front' and nearly lost an eye when it exploded just after switch on - as he was closely examining the circuit. Also when I was young, there was a large bang in my bedroom one night when a smoothing capacitor exploded, bending the aluminium chassis and depositing the inside of the capacitor on the far wall – it was the right way round but the capacitor's working voltage was well below the off-load voltage my newly-designed transmitter power-supply. So make doubly sure your electrolytics are the correct way round *and* their working voltage is high enough. Keep away from them (or wear goggles) when live just to be safe.

Care point (**test equipment**): As to protecting your precious test equipment; always check the range on your multi-meter, making sure it is correct *before* making contact to avoid a costly measurement. Also be aware of maximum DC voltages, the 'max DC input' that instruments such as your signal generator and oscilloscope can stand without damage to their input circuit. Remember that most test equipment these days is designed to test transistorised equipment and so this value might be less than you'd like and below the voltages likely to be encountered on your chassis. If necessary, use a high working voltage external blocking capacitor to protect the input of sensitive test equipment and take measures to ensure that the 'hot' end does not accidentally contact you or the chassis.

7.2 Switch-on

So to the exciting bit. Having worked through all the items that need adding, replacing, cleaning, or lubricating and with all the safety checks completed, the time comes for the big switch-on. I always approach this stage with some apprehension, because occasionally something unforeseen does happen, and one needs to catch it and deal with it before it gets out of hand.

First, temporarily re-fit the control-knobs, including the one for the set's on-off switch. This is for ease of operation and to insulate you from the set in case unexpected voltages are present on the chassis. Ensure the set is 'off', and plug the set into the RCD. If the RCD trips now or later, you will need to unplug the set and investigate the cause; for example an earth leakage current arising from breakdown of the insulation resistance in the mains transformer.

Now switch-on. Applying full voltage, you should be on the alert for the unexpected, as this is when something quite dramatic can happen. The first few seconds are crucial, because if there is anything seriously wrong and an unusually large voltage or current develops, this is when you will notice it. At this critical point, ask yourself urgently about the four S's:

- *Sight* - what can I see – is there any smoke; are any resistors glowing red?
- *Sound* - what can I hear – are there any arcing or sizzling noises?
- *Smell* – is there anything unusual – a pungent odour from a burning resistor or a fused wire?
- *Safety* – what's live and where are my fingers! – am I clear of danger?

Be vigilant for signs of danger; such as the sound of arcing and the sight of overheating components (like droppers) which usually announce their anguish with a glow and a disturbing pong. If something does seem amiss, however trivial, don't be afraid to turn the set off immediately to give yourself some stress-free time to look and think!

Safety Point: Do not touch the chassis! Whatever the type of set, even an earthed one, it could be live and lethal because of a fault!

Next, take a neon mains-test screwdriver and check that it's working - touch it on a live mains contact and confirm that it lights-up. Now, whatever the type of set you're testing, touch this neon mains-test screwdriver on the powered chassis, and observe that it remains *unlit*. If it lights-up, the chassis is live and lethal. You must immediately turn-off (using the insulated knob, and/or manually trip the RCD), disconnect the lead for the mains, and investigate why.

7.3 Fault-Diagnosis

The chances are that switch-on will be an exciting but un-eventful milestone, possibly with of a disappointing lack of life. No matter; having waited at least a minute or two for the set to 'warm-up', we shall assume some sort of fault(s) and do a few checks.

The good news is that if you've sorted out all the problems to this point, the set should be within a gnat's whisker of working. However, you could

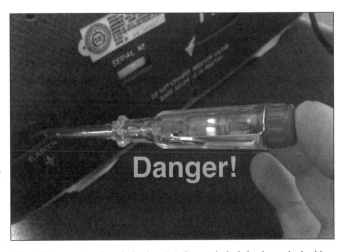

Fig 7.1 **Danger!** – *the whole chassis is live. A lethal shock can be had by touching the exposed metal where the serial number is stamped. Worse, the chassis earth and aerial sockets are both live so any wires connected to them will also be live and could kill someone.*

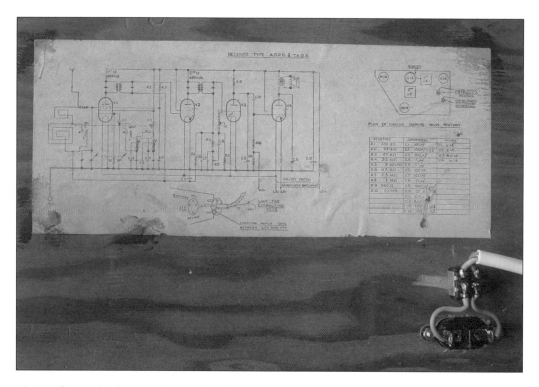

Fig 7.2: This Amplion battery valve portable, already comes with its own circuit diagram - inside the cabinet

now do with access to the circuit diagram. This can be easily obtained for most types of set on CD or by download from specialist suppliers on the internet. It is possible to work to some extent without a circuit diagram, but it does makes life so much easier, not least because of the helpful and essential notes that normally accompany it. This usually includes for example, which coils do what, so that the RF stages can be aligned and the receiver calibrated - this information will be very useful indeed later.

Now check out the circuit in the following order:

1   Are the pilot lamps and valve heaters lit? Sometimes, if a pin isn't sufficiently clean or the holder isn't gripping the base or pin properly a bit of minor remedial action will be required to bring the odd one back to life. Rarely will they all be out, in which case you should chase round with a multi-meter checking that you have the required voltage on the transformer filament-winding tags and see where in the LT circuit the problem lays.

2   Having sorted that out, is there a reassuring mains hum? Assuming that nothing is heard, check the HT voltage is something near to that expected from the circuit diagram (typically 100 – 300V). If it isn't, then take a look at the rectifier (is the valve OK?) and smoothing circuit. In my experience mains transformers are very reliable

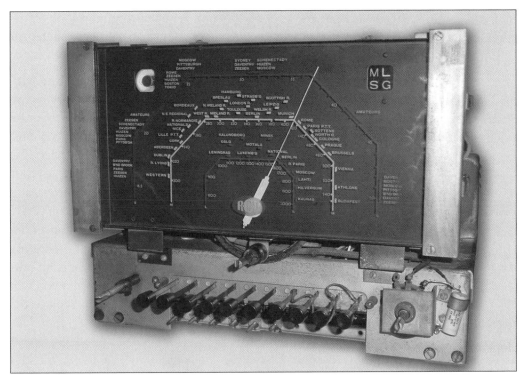

Fig 7.3: An illuminated wave-band indicator indicates presence of the LT. A lit 'Magic-eye' shows the HT is also on

and unlikely to be the cause, but do check the AC winding for the expected voltage. It there an open-circuit somewhere stopping the HT getting to where it should, or worse, a short-circuit drawing current and dragging the HT voltage down?

3   If you have correct HT, chase round and confirm that bias voltages are as expected, and if not, investigate why not. Has the bias resistor changed value, is there a dry joint, is there a problem with the valve on that stage, or is some other component upsetting the bias point? Bear in mind the comments on inter-stage blocking capacitors made earlier, and ensure that the voltage on each control grid is not being uplifted by a capacitor with poor resistive isolation – do change them if in doubt.

4   If it's still quiet, the next step is to feed in a signal to verify (or not, as the case may be!) whether that and subsequent stages are working. Logically it is best to begin with the audio stages and to work back towards the RF input. Taking your RF/AF signal generator, and begin by injecting a 1KHz AF signal at the audio input to check all is well. If so, try injecting an amplitude-modulated (AM) signal further upstream at IF (typically centred somewhere between 455kHz and 465kHz depending on the set), and finally at RF in each waveband. This should reveal which stage is causing a problem. If the problem is at RF, consider whether the Local Oscillator

Fig 7.4: The Pye 906 has no shortage of bulbs to light up its dials and switches. All need to work

is operating, and look for its signal using wave-meter or communications receiver.

Following this path and with good detective-work, you should soon be able to locate and overcome any problems. If you're unable check the electrical condition of your valves with a valve-tester (and most people won't have that facility), and you find a stage which isn't operating properly, and there is no other explanation, then you will probably need to replace the valve in question.

Hopefully, after all this, each dial bulb will be lit up, valves awake with a nice red glow, droppers will be warm (but not glowing!), potentials will be roughly correct, and if you're really lucky, there will be a hum and crackles from the speaker. For our Murphy A70 example, this milestone is reached in **Fig 7.6**.

7.4 Alignment & Calibration

For the purposes of radio restoration we can draw this distinction between 'alignment' and 'calibration': Alignment is about tuning adjustment so that the signal is properly delivered down the chain, whereas calibration is con-

Fig 7.5: Bulbs on and valves lit. A good sign!

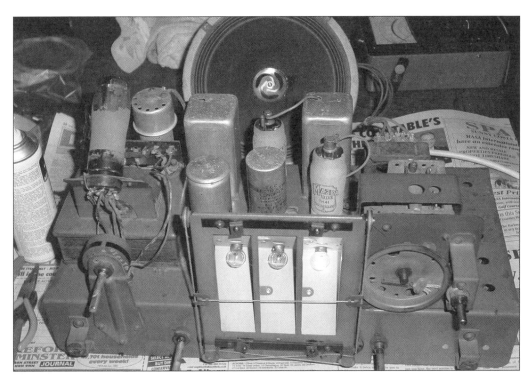

Fig 7.6: *The chassis restored and powered-up*

cerned with ensuring that the dial cursor indicates the actual receive frequency and that it tracks the station markings properly across the tuning dial.

Alignment - My advice is that it is rarely necessary or desirable to interfere with the IF cans whose tuning has been set-up for a pass-band response which is unlikely to have changed. The problem here is that IF stage tuning may be designed to be staggered, providing a 'flat' rather than 'peaked' response in the pass-band.

If the coils have been tampered with, damaged, or values have changed questioning their integrity, then It is possible to use a wobblator (a signal generator which scans the

Fig 7.7: *The inside of an IF can. This one had a break in the middle of a winding, perhaps the result of excessive anode current, caused by failure of grid-block capacitor DC isolation*

IF input while synchronised to an oscilloscope at the IF output) to re-align them and set-up the required response. However, few will have this luxury, and so a simpler alternative is to inject a small AM signal at IF, tune the coils tuned for maximum output, then experiment by detuning them slightly while listening to the result when a broadcast station it tuned in to ensure that the high-frequencies come through as required. Again, don't touch IF tuning unless you really have to.

Alignment of the RF stages involves adjusting the aerial and mixer tuned circuits for best response. For simple receivers the associated trimming capacitors for each waveband can be tuned in the middle of the band for best sensitivity, but for more sophisticated receivers you may need to adjust the trimmers (and possibly coil cores) at two or three frequencies across each waveband so that the sensitivity is evenly distributed across the band. Often the circuit diagram will have notes giving the best tuning sequence to help you, and you should follow its advice in the matter.

Calibration - With the set working nicely you need to check that the stations appear in the right place on the dial. If you haven't already, now is a good time to retrieve the cursor that you previously cleaned and set aside, and to reunite it with its dial cord or tuning shaft. This calibration routine can be quite complicated for the more sophisticated receivers, and the manufacturers notes should be followed if available. Otherwise, connect a few feet of wire to the aerial socket and locate the oscillator trimmer (the one that moves the station when you turn it slightly). Switch to Long Wave and adjust the trimmer so that

Fig 7.8: A potentially daunting array of adjustable flat-trimmers, beehive-trimmers, and iron-cored coils on the underside of the chassis. Each has a purpose!

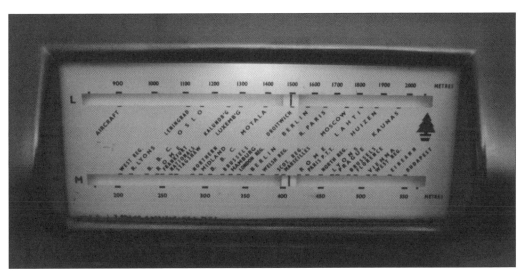

Fig 7.9: *If a dial points to 1500m, it should the set should be listening on 1500m, not 1550m!*

the BBC Radio 4 Long-Wave transmission (formerly the 'Light' Programme) appears at 1500metres (198kHz). Switch to Medium Wave and pick up say Radio 5 Live on 330metres (909kHz) or 433metres (693kHz) and repeat the process using the associated trimmer for this band to place the station at the right position on the tuning dial.

Fig 7.10: *Alignment and calibration complete*

If you have short wave, pick a strong station, note its frequency from announcements or from a frequency-listing guide and repeat the calibration process for this band. The same goes for VHF if you are restoring a 'modern' receiver.

Congratulations - you should now have a receiver that not only works properly, but the stations appear in the right place on the dial.

IT IS WORTH reflecting that what your friends will see and appreciate, apart from the sound, is not the hidden inside workings of the set which you have lovingly restored, but rather, a beautiful cabinet, displaying (I hope) a sparkling dial and shiny knobs. The key here is to know what technique and materials to use to restore that particular type of cabinet. As with the chassis, the plan is NOT to strip the cabinet and start again, but to work sympathetically with what's already there. There are three common types of cabinet: wood, Bakelite and plastic, and we shall discuss the best materials to repair and restore them. The cabinet will usually show some combination of discolouration, scratching, and general neglect, and some skill is required to counter the problems identified without making them worse. The final finish won't be perfect, but using the tips to follow, it should be considerably better than it was.

8.1 Clean and Assess

If you haven't already, take a soft hand-brush to the cabinet and vacuum with a corner-hose attachment (to increase suction) and remove any loose debris. The accumulation will be most evident inside, but pay attention also to nooks and crannies outside, especially underneath where debris can accumulate. Depending on how long and where it has been stored, you may find a large assortment of disgusting material, from dead insects to an extensive network of cobwebs as well as general dust and dirt. Remove all of this grime and then take a break, happy in the knowledge that far more pleasant tasks await!

The next step is to take a look around – are any of the various labels, heat deflectors, and other attachments to the cabinet peeling or hanging off? Do they need re-pinning or gluing back in place? Use panel pins, wood glue, PVA adhesive, plastic adhesive, Araldite, or whatever glue is appropriate for the material in question to bond the two surfaces together to make them secure.

Now examine the speaker cover on both sides: what material is it made of and what is the state of it? Two common materials for this cover are a metal grille and woven fabric (cloth). In the former case, the grille can usually be released and cleaned with convention household metal polish. Sometimes (for example with a Bush DAC90A) the inside of the grille is so clean that it can simply be reversed putting the clean side on view and the dirty side within. If however the cover is fabric your options are probably to leave it in place or to renew it. If it is very dirty, or torn, it will need to be renewed, but happily there are suppliers of such materials, and an acceptable replacement can usually be obtained at low cost. This can be cut out of the sheet supplied and glued onto the inside of the cabinet with an adhesive appropriate to the material to which it will be secured. As to the cabinet itself, there are three main types that you will come across. Let's look at each one in detail.

8.2 Bakelite

This wonderful material, the world's first synthetic plastic, was invented by the Belgian-born American chemist Leo Baekland in 1907 and patented a couple of years later. It was extremely popular in the 1920s & 30s and all manner of objects were made out of it. Radio manufacturers thinking about how to make a really good-looking piece of electrical furniture for the family home soon

Fig 8.1: A restored 'Defiant' Bakelite radio, one of a range sold by the Co-op from 1955

realised that Bakelite has not only good electrical and thermal insulation properties (an essential requirement to house a piece of hot kit with lethal voltages!), but it is also lightweight; certainly when compared to the then traditional wooden cabinet. Moreover, it could be mass produced to a particular shape saving production costs, and provides a beautifully attractive finish for the customer.

Now if you happen to have a radio with a Bakelite cabinet (or any piece of Bakelite for that matter), there is a good chance that it is sitting there looking very dull and not terribly attractive at all. If you try cleaning it, with for example, soapy water, nothing much will happen, except that the surface grime will be removed and it will dry dull again. Happily, there is a

Fig 8.2: An oblique view of this MH356 model of the 'Defiant' range

solution to this which will make your Bakelite as shiny as the day it was made. Some years ago, the GPO (later 'British Telecom') who had rather a lot of Bakelite telephones at the time, developed a special cleaning compound so that its 'phones, such as those in its phone-boxes, could be cleaned quickly and effectively. It is based on the same idea as some car-body cleaning compounds, in that it uses an abrasive paste to remove a very fine layer from the surface to reveal a new and shiny surface. Unlike when you clean silver, the Bakelite surface does not tarnish after a few weeks but remains bright for months if not years. This cleaning material you need is 'Polishing Paste Number 5' (PP5), based on the original recipe, and is available from Greygate chemicals of Coalville, Leicestershire.

Fig 8.3: A tube of PP5 and what the paste looks like

Apply a small dab of this yellow paste from the tube onto the Bakelite via a cloth, work it over the surface, and rub-off. The results are absolutely astonishing if you haven't seen it in action before. Some restorers would add a fine layer of wax afterwards to help retain the shine, and this is an interesting and helpful option if you have the time and the inclination.

As to accompanying Bakelite knobs, if heavily contaminated, clean them first in soapy water, ideally in an ultrasonic bath, as this will do the work for you. Otherwise simply take a duster, apply a dab of PP5, and rub-on and rub-off to reveal a shine. You may

Fig 8.4: A pair of 1920's 'Chad Valley' Bakelite telephones, one cleaned with PP5, to show the difference it makes

find a small buffing wheel on an electric drill helpful in bringing up a shine, but don't try this unless you've practiced on some scrap Bakelite first, and take extreme care that the rotating chuck doesn't come into contact with the piece being cleaned or it will make a nasty scrape or take a chip out. If in doubt, stick to the manual method. Afterwards put to one side on a clean duster ready to refit them later when the chassis is back in the cabinet.

8.3 Plastic

Cleaning of plastic cabinets and especially transparent plastics found in dials,

Fig 8.5: A Bakelite extension-speaker looking resplendent after its clean with PP5

needs to be attempted with extreme caution, as applying the wrong solvent can have a very dramatic effect - in a bad and irrecoverable way. One of the most trust-worthy and effective formulations that I have used is the 'Plastic Polish' available from Greygate chemicals. This thick, white, highly pungent liquid I have found to be excellent at cleaning plastics and was even successful at removing mistiness from a plastic tuning window (it works on cloudy car headlights too!). A more widely available alternative that can give good results is foam cleaner (with ammonia). If you don't have these, you can try instead one of the innumerable

Fig 8.6 The Speaker Manufacturer's 'Rees Mace' logo

house-hold plastic cleaners available from your local shop, but with any formulation, try it on an inconspicuous area first, just to be sure that there is no adverse effect. Another option is to use a fine abrasive on a calico mop attached to an electric drill, but as with Bakelite, this approach requires some skill and care in its execution and should not be attempted unless you have practised on a scrap piece first.

You may be tempted to apply your favourite solvent (Isopropyl alcohol, acetone, methylated spirit, white spirit etc), but there is a significant risk that it may react with the plastic. Depending on what type

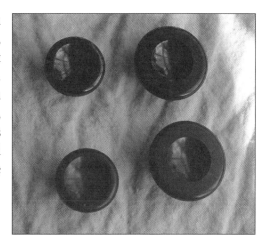

Fig 8.7: *Bakelite knobs from a Cossor radio cleaned and ready for fitting*

Fig 8.8: *Cloudiness removed from the plastic cover, yielding a beautifully clear dial as befits this lovely Amplion battery portable*

it is, the plastic may suffer a range of adverse symptoms from surface blooming and crazing to turning clear plastic opaque. Please don't apply unless you've tried the solvent on an obscure area first to assess its suitability.

As to plastic knobs, windows, and any small and intricate parts, remove these from safe-keeping in your bits jar and if necessary clean first with soapy water to remove surface grime. I find an ultrasonic bath ideal for this activity. Take out, dry roughly with a kitchen towel, and allow to dry naturally. Don't try to speed-up the process by placing the plastic parts on a radiator as it may warp them (as I've discovered). Beware also that lettering and numbering on plastic parts can be easily wiped off by the cleaning action, so take extra care where these are present. Now apply plastic polish to these items and rub-off for a nice finish.

8.4 Wood

Unlike Bakelite and plastic cabinets, wooden cabinets are a natural 'living' material. Woodworm, by definition like to live in such surroundings and if your cabinet has an array of 0.5mm holes in it, they have probably enjoyed their visit and made it their home. The first task then is to apply a standard woodworm treatment using an aerosol available from your local hardware store. You will probably want to do this outside because of the smell but also to avoid the risk of woodworm moving house from your cabinet into your living-room furniture.

The large heavy wooden cabinet is a feature of late 1920s-1940s wirelesses and should be their crowning glory. Although primarily functional in protecting the

Fig 8.9: *Woodworm flight-holes in this RGD cabinet – treat outside with woodworm treatment as a matter of urgency in case the woodworm are still alive and are contemplating moving.*

user from lethal voltages and providing an interface to the equipment through various dials and knobs, cabinets were intended to look really good sitting in the living room or parlour. Like the modern car, purchase was as much, if not more, about looks as performance. Manufacturers knew this and considerable effort was put into making cabinets that looked the part. Presentation is everything, and so when restoring the cabinet, the aim must be to get back to something approaching its original looks.

Fig 8.10: *A glorious Pye PE69 looking good after a bit of attention*

Fig 8.11: *My HMV bought at auction for 5 shillings (25p) in the late 1960s. Great for listening to pirate radio stations illicitly broadcasting pop music. A treasured item in need of expert TLC.*

Examine the outside of the cabinet. You will probably notice a whole variety of scratch and knock marks acquired over the years, and perhaps also some staining, often concentrated on top, as wooden cabinets are invariably square or oblong and most people cannot resist the urge to put something (like a plant pot) on top of it. This is doubly unfortunate if you have a logo showing Nipper listening to his master's voice on your HMV set, or a rising

Fig 8.12: *An RGD set before treatment*

Fig 8.13: *An RGD set after treatment – not perfect but a lot better*

Fig 8.15: *The finished restoration – outside*

sun logo on your Pye set as it is likely to be scuffed and possibly obliterated. Furthermore, you may not be aware at this stage that the wooden surface bleaches over time and it actually appears to you much lighter than it should.

The good news is that a considerable improvement to the general appearance of the set can be had quickly and easily. There is a 'magic' solution which restorers use called a 'reviving mixture' which does exactly what it says. It has a dramatic effect as it cleans, reverses bleaching, and gives a deep and glorious shine to the wood's surface. Although you can purchase a Reviving Mixture ready-made, it is really easy (and much cheaper) to create your own. Pour equal parts of methylated spirit, white spirit, and boiled linseed

oil into a jar with a screw-on lid. You will notice a distinct purple layer associated with the methylated spirit, a clear layer from the white spirit, and clear or slightly pale-yellow layer from the linseed oil. Tighten the lid and shake vigorously. It will suddenly change colour to something similar to salad cream. Please don't forget to label the bottle to say what it is, and that it's poisonous! Apply with a soft lint-free cloth immediately to the wood. Be generous, and observe how the surface changes from light, dull, dirty, and lifeless, to a darker shade which is clean and vibrant,

Fig 8.14: *The finished restoration – inside*

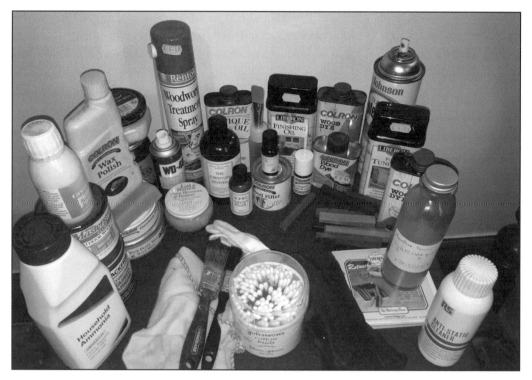

Fig 8.16: An array of materials and implements that can come in useful when trying to restore a cabinet

showing-off the colour of the wood (often mahogany). It can be a wonderful transformation if you haven't witnessed it before!

Turning to the various scratches, score marks, and chips, the plan here is to try and make them as inconspicuous as possible. It is a difficult task to execute properly, which gets only a little easier with experience. Where there are deep score marks, or small chips missing, one approach is to apply wood filler, smooth off and apply wood stain of the nearest shade. For shallower damage, it may be possible to run some commercial furniture restoring liquid of the right shade along the line of the scratch, or use to a wax stick, again of the right shade, to fill-up the scratch line. It is best to apply some thought as to how to tackle your particular scenario and by trial and error using these different methods and materials, arrive at the best result. Finally, you may wish to rub a good wax over the cabinet to enhance and protect the finish.

For our Murphy example the finished product is shown in **Fig 8.14** and **Fig 8.15**.

For further advice on restoring wood, see the excellent little book by Bonner [3]

Completing the Job

SOME CABINETS may incorporate a clear tuning window(s) because stations are marked on a background on the removed chassis, in which case, clean the cabinet windows using glass cleaner, and if provided with a Bakelite surround, clean this using the material and method described in the section on Bakelite.

Check whether the underside of the cabinet has, or should have by the marks remaining, cloth feet to avoid damaging the surface that it sits on. Replace any missing feet with a modern equivalent for furniture or a salvaged period part.

Any knobs which you have safely stored in your bits jar should now be cleaned. Normally made of Bakelite or plastic rather than wood, use the advice given earlier to clean these materials.

Having restored the chassis assembly and got it working satisfactorily, and having renovated the cabinet to something like its original glory, it's time to recombine the two.

9.1 Final Assembly

Ensure that any separate paxolin interface boards for aerial, earth, and gram, have been cleaned and are in place. If you have a cabinet speaker and have removed it, now

it the time to put it back – a process which is often easier said than done. When offering the retaining clamps to the speaker, take care not to drop the speaker in your manoeuvring or put your finger through the cone! Likewise, if you're putting a nice clean tuning glass back in, take extreme care not to knock, drop, or crack it during your manoeuvres. The glass is likely to be held in place by metal pushing against rubber cushions. These cushions will often have perished (as discussed in the section on 'glassware clean') and will need replacing with new ones, perhaps taken from a grommet or some other rubber or soft plastic item. Be very careful indeed that the pressure on the glass is kept even, and do not to overtighten the screws, or the glass will crack with devastating consequences for your morale.

Fig 9.1: *An Ultra 'Lynx' chassis ready to go back into its cabinet*

Fig 9.2: The Ultra 'Lynx' chassis safely inside its cabinet

Now, working on a sturdy, stable, and level surface, reinsert the chassis into its cabinet and reconnect any loudspeaker, frame aerial and interface boards (if the leads are long enough it may be easier to reconnect before reinsertion). Recover the screws and washers from your jar, and with care and thought, draw one end over the edge of the work surface so that you can access the underside of the cabinet and insert the first retaining screw and washer. Holding a heavy cabinet while blindly pushing up the screw, moving the chassis and trying to locate the required chassis hole by feel, all at the same time, can be an awkward exercise and an accident waiting to happen. Take your time, think ahead, and call-in an extra pair of hands to help if they are available.

Recover any knobs that you've set aside from your bits jar and clean them using the procedure noted in the preceding sections on plastic and Bakelite as appropriate. Take care not to inadvertently remove the markings by observing the advice given previously.

With the restored set almost complete, fit these knobs and any cloth spacers, which are used to stop knobs rubbing on the cabinet. If you can, replace any that are missing, otherwise tighten the retaining screw, but consciously leave a gap sufficiently wide to prevent the knob rubbing on the cabinet.

Finally, locate the back cover and clean it initially with a soft brush and vacuum. Next, if it's made of solid wood, restore as for the cabinet proper, otherwise (which will usually be the case), if it's made of a thick card type with ventilation holes, use a lint-free cloth to apply a

Fig 9.3: Ultra 'Lynx' with knobs refitted

Fig 9.5: *The much more common ventilated 'thick card' back*

Fig 9.4: *The rear of the 'lynx' showing its wooden back*

squirt of cheap household furniture cleaner from an aerosol. This will remove surface dust and give it a bit of lustre.

Stick down any labels that are peeling, or have peeled off, and fit the back onto the set. Replace any missing washers on the fixing screws to complete the job.

You should now have one fully working and resplendent-looking old radio (or wireless!)

9.2 Care & Maintenance

You may have noticed that we have taken care to restore, not rebuild the set. Restoration requires some skill in assessing what has to be replaced and what is able to be left. This approach keeps as much of the original set as possible, but means that maintenance will be necessary from time to time as components further deteriorate or fail. Rebuild is a simpler 'blunderbuss' approach, where virtually everything electrical is replaced and wooden cabinets are completely stripped, stained and varnished in the process. Restoration largely keeps the original item, whereas rebuilding largely destroys it and generates a new product. With an ever decreasing pool of original sets, restorers keen to preserve our heritage might well regard the rebuild approach as an anathema, for it destroys for ever that which could be preserved. However, to be fair, if someone doesn't have the time, expertise, or facilities needed for a full restoration, but they are prepared to undertake the effort required for a rebuild, much better this than the set being confined to the skip!

Having decided to restore, we must consider future failure by reviewing the types of vintage component that we have kept and consider which are likely to need attention in the future. As a general rule, and perhaps in a rough order of appearance, we can identify these as typical faults waiting to happen:

Fig 9.6: A finished item

1. Intermittent or 'noisy' volume and tone controls and waveband switches

2. Dial cord slipping/stalling /breaking

3. Loss of output or sensitivity caused by low valve emission

4. Loss of output or sensitivity caused by failure (DC isolation) of grid blocking capacitor

5. Abnormal mains hum from electrolytic capacitor failure

6. Set failure arising from mains dropper or HT dropper failure

All of these can be tackled as they arise using the practical and diagnostic techniques discussed earlier to return the set to working order. Obviously, care of the cabinet is also a concern, and while occasional cleaning with a duster and some furniture polish will be sufficient, longer term, you may want to re-apply the techniques for Bakelite, plastic, or wood as appropriate in order to bring the set's appearance back up to par. Books such as that by Jackson & Day [4] can be helpful for specialist advice on restoring specific materials.

As to use; 'little and often' is a good rule as this helps to keeps the electrolytics fresh and ensures the set is not overworked. To be extra safe, don't leave a vintage set running, especially in the family environment, without a responsible adult present. Many were not expected to be run '24/7' and some get very hot indeed as a result of thermal dissipation from valves, mains droppers, and other components. Keep it away from flammable furnishings and please don't put a saucer of water with a plant in on top!

Now you have a lovely working set, relax, enjoy, and show it off to your friends!

References

[1] Fairchild Semiconductor, 1N4007 Datasheet, Downloaded 1st January 2016

[2] Hammond Engineering, Design Guide for Rectifier Use, Downloaded 1st January 2016

[3] Kevin Jan Bonner, Furniture Restoration, Guild of Master Craftsman Publications Ltd, 1998

[4] Albert Jackson & David Day, Care and Repair of Antiques and Collectables, Collins, 2006

Appendix

Using a Multimeter – for Beginners

THIS IS a basic measuring instrument that every electronics enthusiast should have. Available as a digital or an analogue type, both sorts have their pros and cons, and so ideally you would have one of each. You can now buy a really good, brand new, multimeter of either variety for as little as £10-£20, which is fantastic value for money, although as with most things, the more you pay, the more features, better precision, and higher quality you get. A basic multimeter will measure voltage, resistance and current. A better one could measure inductance, capacitance, temperature, and frequency as well, and might even incorporate an AF signal generator. Let's look more closely at what can be measured, how, and things to look out for......

Fig A1.1: *A basic low-cost digital multimeter*

Voltage: A modern digital multimeter (**Fig A1.2**) is capable of measuring a steady AC or DC voltage extremely accurately because its 'loading' effect on the circuit is normally negligible, and because it presents the result clearly on a display with large numbers. The analogue type in contrast (**Fig A1.2**) will usually 'load' the circuit more (a high 'ohms-per-volt' rating reduces this effect), and the needle position is harder to interpret although some multimeters have a mirror behind the needle so that it can be read 'head on' (ie no parallax). That said, the analogue multimeter is often superior where the voltage is moving, as fluctuations can be followed far more easily. For the restoration of old valve radio sets, I would prefer the latter for voltage measurements for the reasons given, and additionally because if there is AC (mains hum) on the DC (HT) supply, a digital multimeter can get very confused and give a variable and misleading readout. Beware also, that the working range of many digital multimeters may extend to only to a few tens, rather than hundreds of volts, because they are intended to test modern transistorised equipment, and so are not suitable for the task. Either way, when you pick up those two probes, know the highest voltage likely to be encountered and set the multimeter to a suitable range before making a measurement.

Fig A1.2: *A medium-cost analogue multimeter with anti-parallax mirror*

If you don't, you may trigger the 'quick-blow' fuse, damage the instrument, and (if analogue) permanently bend the needle or burn-out the movement.

Current: Similar arguments apply - ideally the working range should extend to at least a few amps.

Resistance: A digital multimeter can give a quick and accurate result. However, when measuring large resistances (say >1M ohm) ensure that the multimeter's internal resistance (shown in its specification) is at least 10x the resistance that you're trying to measure (and preferably a lot more) to minimize shunt errors. Cheaper multimeters may have an internal resistance of only 10M ohm, the best ones 10G ohms.

Never attempt to measure resistance with the power on, and ensure that one end of the resistor is disconnected from the circuit to avoid a false reading caused by other components shunted across it. To avoid errors when measuring low resistances, ensure that your probes are clean and well-fitted at the other end. Bringing the two probes together, an analogue multimeter should go roughly full-scale: use the 'zero' knob to manually set the pointer to '0 ohms' on the dial (**Fig A1.3**). Make good use of the parallax mirror if provided. A digital multimeter should auto-zero, or show a small resistance (<1 ohm at the most).

Fig A1.3: Setting 0-ohms prior to resistance measurement

Inductance and Capacitance: Connect the isolated component to the probes or slots provided. Remember that any test leads inherently have a small self-inductance along them and a small self-capacitance across them. This 'parasitic' value should be noted and subtracted from the item being tested if it significant in comparison.

Fig A1.4: Checking resistance of the test leads

Temperature: Sometimes a thermocouple on a twisted-pair cable is provided which plugs into the multimeter. Note the thermocouple temperature range, and secure with tape, and possibly heat-sink compound, to the item to be measured.

Frequency measurement: An in-built frequency counter may allow limited in-circuit frequency measurement via the test probes. Do not exceed the maximum specified voltage between the probes when connecting to a powered set in this mode. Normally intended for probing transistorised equipment, you may need an external capacitor (DC block) with a high DC working voltage to protect the multimeter.

Signal-Generator: This may usefully provide a basic AF waveform (perhaps sine, square, triangular, or sawtooth) to the probes. Again, do not exceed the maximum specified voltage between the probes when injecting a signal into a powered-up set; use an external DC block if necessary.

Fig A1.5: A quality analogue multimeter that is a pleasure to use

Handling a nice multimeter is one of the joys of electrical restoration and maintenance. If you understand how it works and use it correctly, your joy will be complete and you will have mastered a basic competence essential to any electrical work.